# THE WOODLAND YEAR

Ben Law

Published by

Permanent Publications
Hyden House Ltd
The Sustainability Centre
East Meon
Hampshire GU32 1HR
United Kingdom
Tel: 01730 776 582
Overseas: (international code +44 - 1730)
Email: enquiries@permaculture.co.uk
Web: www.permanentpublications.co.uk



Reprinted 2019

Designed and typeset by Tim Harland

Front cover photograph by John Adams

Printed in the UK by CPI Antony Rowe, Chippenham, Wiltshire

All paper from FSC certified mixed sources

The Forest Stewardship Council (FSC) is a non-profit international organisation established to promote the responsible management of the world's forests. Products carrying the FSC label are independently certified to assure consumers that they come from forests that are managed to meet the social, economic and ecological needs of present and future generations.

British Library Cataloguing-in-Publication Data

A catalogue record for this book is available from the British Library

ISBN 978 1 85623 331 9

## Tree Cycles

When I first felled you
I was a young man,
Eagerly I watched you crash to the ground
I only glanced at the hidden rings
No other had seen
I now stare at in middle age

How many have you warmed through winter's cold
How many houses hold your limbs
Holding up roofs for those who never knew you
How many cattle have you penned within the field
How many have eaten from your table and sat upon your chair?

Next time I fell you will be my last
Not yours, you will see many others, young and headstrong
Middle aged and reflective, old and frail
All taking what you so freely give

*Ben Law*

# CONTENTS

Hear the voice of the Bard!
Who Present, Past, and Future sees;
Whose ears have heard,
The Holy Word,
That walked among the ancient trees

William Blake from 'Songs of Experience'

Foreword

# Hugh Fearnley-Whittingstall

I first met Ben in Prickly Nut Wood almost 15 years ago. He'd been living there, in a bender and teepee for a couple of years, I think. I was making my first television programme, A Cook on the Wild Side, and I dropped in for a few tips on living off the land. I learned how to make birch sap wine, helped Ben burn a batch of charcoal, and watched him work his wooden pole lathe. We ended up drinking an assortment of his hedgerow brews around the fire. Let's be honest, we ended up drunk.

It was all good fun, and made a charming five minute segment for the show. But I took something away from that day with Ben that was hard to express in the programme (though I tried). I went away with a new found conviction that has never left me: wood matters. In fact, in terms of how it nurtures us, it's right up there with food and water. And, as with those two elemental forces for survival, the way we deal with wood is part of what defines us, both as individuals, and, ultimately, as a species.

Every child knows that there's no better toy than a stick. And every adult who forgets the immediate, dependable companionship, both practical and spiritual, of a piece of wood, either in its raw state, or formed for function, will lose something precious. The man or woman who never stops to admire the shape of a tree, or the grain of a tabletop, is too busy to be truly alive. We can't all know and love wood with the deep passion and profound understanding that Ben has. But we all can, and indeed must, let it into our lives, as a force for good.

If you think that sounds far fetched, or pompous – or you just don't get it – then read this book and I'm sure you will. Because one of Ben's remarkable gifts, besides being arguably Britain's greatest living woodsman, is a knack for inspiring others, both as a writer, and by example.

*The Woodland Year* is a month-by-month journey through Ben's woodland in the Sussex Weald, and a celebration of every aspect of sustainable woodland management. The cycles of nature, the seasonal tasks, wild food gathering, hedgerow wine making (I can vouch for the quality and strength), genuinely useful and tempting recipes, coppice crafts, timber frame eco-building, nature conservation, species diversity... it's all here. But it's never over-detailed, exclusive or patronising – it's always clear, fresh and empowering.

But *The Woodland Year* offers more than this. As an intimate account of Ben's yearly cycle of work, his naturally tuned lifestyle and deep immersion in the very fabric of the nature of his woods, it's beguiling and somehow irresistible.

Ben generously invites all his readers to partake of his discoveries. In words that are often lyrical but always ungilded, he describes a way of life that is both economically and ecologically viable. As such, it holds some of the fundamental keys to how we can achieve a more sustainable, lower carbon society.

In the end it is Ben's absolute passion for woodlands, as well as wood, which is the mark of the man. His deep understanding of them is now opening up many regenerative possibilities for the British landscape and would-be woodlanders alike. By training others in woodland skills, by using his woods and house to educate many, by writing books such as this, by putting himself in the media spotlight – a place that by his humble nature isn't the most comfortable place for him to be – Ben has dedicated his life to showing that looking after our woodlands is essential for our future material well-being.

Ben is a true pioneer and is, by example, quite simply creating a woodland renaissance in Britain. Read this, and you will surely want to be part of it.

# Explanation

It is with intention that this book begins in November. This is the point from which all woodsman start and where all products flow.

As in my book *The Woodland Way,* I have regularly used the word 'man' in this text as in 'woodsman'. This is not a reference to gender, and this book should highlight that men and woman are equally capable of woodland activities. It comes from *manus,* the Latin word meaning hand. Thus woodsman means 'hand of the woods'.

My choice of trees for the twelve months has no ancient or symbolic reference. They are my personal choice of twelve trees amongst many which I use, manage and enjoy within the woodland year.

The food and wine recipes are some of my own making but others have been adapted from recipes or borrowed from friends with a similar interest in wild food. Where there is a direct connection to the source of the recipe this has been credited. I have tried to balance the recipes between those that you may sit down and have as a main meal and those that are simply prepared and cooked over the fire.

The contributors who have kindly shared their woodland experience with you are a few of many. We are a growing number who are turning to a positive and practical way of life at a time of global uncertainty. I have avoided editing the individual contributions (except for the reducing in size of some of the longer pieces) as I wanted you to hear the voice of the contributors. Their views are not necessarily the same as mine, but together it gives a stronger picture of those who are living the cycle of 'the woodland year'.

My choice in wine making is to make woodland wines of lower sugar content than many. This produces a wine of good flavour and slightly drier than many of the well sugared recipes you may come across. I have not mentioned yeast nutrient in my recipes, but with some of the flower wines you may wish to add a little malt extract (10ml to a gallon), or a commercial yeast nutrient, to ensure all the sugar ferments fully out.

I grew up in an era which saw the change from imperial to metric. I feel fortunate in this timing as I see it as knowing two languages. Although where possible I have used metric measurements in the text, there are places in the forestry, wine making and construction worlds where imperial is still the dominant force in the UK. If I am laying out floor joists on a building, they are likely to be 6 x 2 in at 400mm centres. These variations which may occur within the text can be translated through the imperial to metric conversion table on the next page. Please feel thankful I did not get into forestry measurements of cords and hoppus feet!

**Warning!** All the information on plants and fungi contained in this book is given in good faith on the understanding that all good sense is used in the use of them. However, neither I or the publisher can accept responsibility for wrongly identified plants or fungi consumed by the reader, or any allergic reaction caused by them. I strongly recommend therefore you make sure you have identified it correctly – using cross referenced botanical identification. If you have any doubt, don't eat it.

## General Conversion Formulae

| From | To | Multiply by |
|---|---|---|
| inches | millimetres | 25.4 |
| millimetres | inches | 0.0394 |
| inches | centimetres | 2.54 |
| centimetres | inches | 0.3937 |
| feet | metres | 0.3048 |
| metres | feet | 3.281 |
| yards | metres | 0.9144 |
| metres | yards | 1.094 |
| sq inches | sq centimetres | 6.452 |
| sq centimetres | sq inches | 0.155 |
| sq metres | sq feet | 10.76 |
| sq feet | sq metres | 0.0929 |
| sq yards | sq metres | 0.8361 |
| sq metres | sq yards | 1.196 |
| acres | hectares | 0.4047 |
| hectares | acres | 2.471 |
| pints | litres | 0.5682 |
| litres | pints | 1.76 |
| gallons | litres | 4.546 |
| litres | gallons | 0.22 |
| ounces | grams | 28.35 |
| grams | ounces | 0.03527 |
| pounds | grams | 453.6 |
| grams | pounds | 0.002205 |
| pounds | kilograms | 0.4536 |
| kilograms | pounds | 2.205 |

# Photo Credits

All photographs in this book are taken by, and/or are the copyright of, Ben Law and likewise those in each monthly contributors' section by the individual contributor, with the exception of the following:

**Front cover** *John Adams*
**Back cover** *John Adams*
**Back cover background** *Ben Law*
*Backgrounds to tree profiles in each month: Penny Rose*
**7** *River Cottage*
**15** *Recipe middle: W. Robinson & Son (Seeds & Plants) Ltd*
**33** *Bob Atkins*
**35** *Top & bottom: Bob Atkins*
**36** *Bottom: Bob Atkins*
**57** *Tree profile, top: Penny Rose, bottom: Tim Harland*
**70** *Top & bottom: Helen Healey, www.helenhealeyphotography@virgin.net*
**71** *Top: Helen Healey, bottom: Ben Law*
**72** *Top and bottom right: Helen Healey, bottom left: Ben Law*
**80** *Top right: Roger Whiteway*
**84** *Tree profile, top: Penny Rose*
**86** *Middle and bottom: Ben Law*
**93** *Bottom left: Maddy Harland*
**98** *Bottom: Tim Harland*
**111** *Bottom: Ben Law*
**113** *Danny Chapman, www.rowlhouse.freeserve.co.uk*
**114** *John Adams*
**115** *Right, top: Jens Stolt / Shutterstock*
**116** *Bottom left: Sergy Chushkin / Shutterstock*
**117** *Tree profile, top: Roger Whiteway*
**119** *Tree profile, above right: Penny Rose*
**148** *Top: Pestalozzi*
**154** *John Adams*
**156** *John Adams*

Special thanks to Penny Rose and John Adams at Permanent Publications for their help in filling the photographic gaps and to Jess Upton at River Cottage HQ for help with supplying the photo accompanying Hugh's Foreword.

# Introduction

The seasonal synchronicity of life in the woods never ceases to amaze me. What other working relationship is so well adapted and in harmony with the changing seasons? On the coldest days of winter, the comfort of a brash fire and the natural gym of a working woodland keeps me warm and healthy, spring heralds the transition from the cutting and the more physical work into the creative craftwork of summer, and autumn's harvest of wild food and the gathering of firewood prepares me for the cycle of the year to begin once more.

I hope this book gives you an insight into the cycle of woodland life. As you journey with me through a woodland year at Prickly Nut Wood, each month we will depart and meet other woodlanders elsewhere, working and living in a particular phase of their woodland year.

This book celebrates the woods and woodland living, but it is not my intention to over romanticise life in the woods. My life as a woodsman is physically demanding, often quite poorly paid and winter on these heavy clay Wealden soils can throw up many challenges as I try to extract timber with an extra kilo of soil on each boot. But even within the muddy depths of winter the quality of lifestyle shines through. After four grey wet days in the coppice, the sun rises and the leaf mould steams beneath the trees like the nostrils of a horse, the sound of the bird song fills the air and I become aware once more of the magic of my surroundings and the privilege of working in the woodland environment. Seasonal treats of wild food; satisfaction of the creativity of craftwork and seeing the regeneration of the woodland, wild flowers and butterflies returning is a reward not measurable in economic terms. This life is wholesome and above all connects me to a sense of place, a deep understanding of the land and its seasonal changes. This sense of belonging in the natural rhythm of life gives me a tangible sense of purpose rarely available in the modern workplace.

I have lived at Prickly Nut Wood for only sixteen years, yet I can confidently make the statement 'I know this wood better than any other human on this planet'. This is a bold statement indeed but one that identifies how poorly we know our landscape. My small but ever growing knowledge as a woodsman and forest dweller is just a taste of real knowledge of the land. I know where to find mushrooms. I can tell you almost to the day when the first nightjar of the year will sing. I know where the deer rest and which oak will be the first to break leaf in spring. I can create wine from trees and a house from sticks but when I travel to a forest where the forest dwellers have lived for many generations, their sense of knowledge of their place shows up the limits of my sixteen years at Prickly Nut Wood. We must start somewhere, however, and each rotation of the year brings new depths of knowledge and understanding.

Within each season there are true wonders to behold; the awakening of spring flowers, the arrival of flying migrants, glimpses of rare butterflies, the visual fire of autumn and the silence of the woodland snow.

Within our woodlands a voice is calling, echoing an ancient knowledge of the land from the roots to the tips. I invite you to join me and step into the cycle of the woodland year.

NOVEMBER

# NOVEMBER in Prickly Nut Wood

The last of the leaf is falling away and the distinct dark shapes of the sweet chestnut stems begin to reveal their potential. I am choosing which cants to cut. I have orders for yurt poles, rustic fencing, arbours, planks for a boardwalk, poles for roundwood building and frames for woven fencing. Other orders will come, so I choose carefully. Once selected and the cutting has begun, the chosen areas must be completed before spring.

I choose two cants; one, an acre of coppice which I last cut five years ago and the other about 2½ acres of much older coppice. After cutting a stem and counting the rings I find it was forty-one years since it was last cut. My mind wanders back to forty-one years ago and I think of the woodsmen and what they were cutting the timber for. Probably hop poles, we drank more beer then, but now there is little demand for hop poles, so much of the hops used are imported. I expect they made some pales for chestnut paling fencing; it has been the backbone of the chestnut coppice industry for some years now. I too will make some pales from this year's cut. I expect it was cut with an axe last time, more peaceful than the chainsaw I am using. I look around for objects from the last cut. Old bottles are a regular find as can be the remnants of an old pair of boots. I find neither but come across a toothed Allen scythe blade embedded between two trees, the remains of a cleaving brake. This is a sure sign that the poles were split down and I feel confident that the woodsmen were making pales forty-one years ago on the spot where I am now standing.

It is time for me to share my work and ways of the woods with others once more. My 'apprentices' for this woodland year have arrived. They arrive with expectations, eagerness and a few belongings. Working clothes, a musical instrument, torch and a few books, innocently unaware of what winter may throw at us. If they are still here in the summer they will have gone through an initiation into a woodland lifestyle, an experience from which most never return to the life they had before. Their accommodation is basic, a small caravan or yurt. A winter under canvas is more comfortable than people imagine, with a good wood-burning stove you will be warmer than in many houses.

***November title page: Sweet chestnut coppice last cut forty-one years ago.***

## Cleaving

Cleaving is the process where unsawn timber is split by forcing the fibres apart across its length. Cleaved wood is stronger by virtue of the fact that the fibres are unsawn. There are many different designs of cleaving brake, the purpose of which is to act as a vice so that the woodsman can control the split so that it runs evenly down the log. If the split begins to run out to one side of the log, by putting downward pressure on the thicker section, the split will return to a central position.

***Right: Cleaving chestnut in a brake with a froe.***

Returning home with Oily (my lurcher), I cut through an area of overstood coppice and I am greeted by an unexpected surprise. My eye casts upon a mass of black/grey fungus and as my vision focuses, I realise I am standing amidst a sea of 'Black Trumpet', also known as 'Horn of Plenty' (*Craterellus Cornucopioides*). I note my position and return to the house for two large baskets and spend the next hour harvesting this gastronomic delight. With two full baskets and plenty left in the woods I visit a couple of local restaurants and trade my wares. The popularity of wild food is increasing. Woodlands provide an unusual variety of untampered, unfarmed natural food and once you get to know your local chefs, they will usually be more than happy to take all surplus wild mushrooms and other

***Above: Horn of Plenty.***

***Recipe top: Basket of freshly picked Horn of Plenty.***

***Recipe middle: Kale, 'Nero de Toscana'.***

***Recipe bottom: Nero's trumpet.***

## Nero's Trumpet

This recipe is one that combines my passion for wild fungi and good wintergreens. The variety of kale, 'Nero de Toscana', has a slight peppered flavour and with its attractive deep green thin leaves it brings freshness to the winter table. We are usually harvesting it from early October through to March. It forms the perfect bed to pour on the creamy Horn of Plenty.

Two large handfuls of Horn of Plenty
(or substitute with chanterelle mushrooms)
Twenty leaves of Nero de Toscana
One clove garlic
Olive oil
Small pot of fresh cream
Salt and pepper
Lemon juice
Fresh thyme and parsley

Slice the Nero de Toscana into thin strips and steam for four minutes. Take a heavy frying pan and fry finely chopped garlic in the olive oil. Chop Horn of Plenty and fry for a few minutes add seasoning and lemon juice. Stir cream in slowly and add chopped thyme and parsley simmer for a minute then pour over the bed of Nero de Toscana.

wild food as well. The volume of Horn of Plenty allows me the opportunity to dry a few kilos above the woodburner ensuring I will have a good supply to see me through the year.

The flavour of Horn of Plenty is so distinctive even a small amount will flavour soups and stews but my favourite recipe is one I call 'Nero's Trumpet', *see previous page*.

The nights are drawing in now and all daylight hours must be used. Unlike summer, our lunch breaks are short. We get cold if we sit around outside so it is better to keep on the move. The hooting of the tawny owls marks long winter nights at Prickly Nut Wood. On clear moonlit nights a hooting Olympics could be underway, the volume of the calls making it difficult to calculate how many owls are involved. I know many of their haunts and often notice them in the daytime masquerading as a dead branch. They are a beautiful bird, so silent in flight and important in keeping numbers of mice and rats in check. They drop pellets that contain the indigestible remnants of fur and bones and, in one investigation, 700 owl pellets were examined and found to contain 2,513 mice!

Every year as I begin the winter's cut, I am moved. I feel a stirring within me as if I am making contact with generations past and future as I know this wonderful resource will come of age again. Once we realise the importance of purchasing local products to support the management of our local woods and understand the huge energy cost of timber miles, coppice woodlands will get the recognition they deserve. Many of our coppiced woodlands have been managed for hundreds of years to create unique ecosystems producing sustainable timber, rural employment and a hugely biodiverse environment.

## Coppice

Coppice is the term used to describe the successional cutting of broadleaf woodland during the dormant winter period. In spring, when the sap rises, the stump (known as the stool) sends up new shoots that are grown on for a number of years until they reach the desired size. They are then cut again during winter and the process repeats itself. The wood cut from coppice is known as 'underwood' and has for centuries supplied a variety of traditional products and supported a large rural workforce, from cutter to coppice merchant, craftsman to purchaser.

Coppice is a valuable crop and, managed well, can sustain more people per acre than any of the modern forestry alternatives. It is also a sustainable pattern of management, rarely needing any replanting, leaving the soil undisturbed and therefore not subject to the risks of erosion. Nutrients are returned primarily through the annual leaf fall. Coppice creates a cyclical habitat and unique ecosystem, and is one of the few patterns of symbiosis known in nature where humans are an important part of the relationship. In a well-managed coppice, the stools are closely spaced, from about 4-6 feet apart and the ground is fully shaded by the leaves and coppice shoots. When the coppice is cut, sunlight pours in, dormant seeds waiting for light emerge and different birds, animals and butterflies move into the re-emerged habitat.

***Below: Sweet chestnut coppice.***

# Sweet Chestnut (*Castanea sativa*)

It is presumed that sweet chestnut was introduced by the Romans and it is accepted as an 'honorary native' tree on the grounds that it is a historic member of our flora and enters into the natural vegetation.

*Ground conditions:*
Prefers acid soil pH 4.0-4.5 with sandy or silty soil (20% clay). Greensand is seen as optimum soil type. Avoid frost pockets.

*Silvicultural practice:*
Most commonly grown as coppice predominantly in the south-east of England. Standards tend to suffer from ring shake making much of the timber unsuitable for saw logs. Larger coppice stems can be milled and as there is virtually no sapwood, a small diameter pole can still produce useful boards.

***Area of sweet chestnut coppice by region Forestry Commission census 1979-1982***

|  |  |
|---|---|
| Kent | 12,544 |
| East Sussex | 3,349 |
| West Sussex | 1,393 |
| Elsewhere in south-east England | 780 |
| South-west England | 399 |
| East England | 584 |
| Northern England | 42 |
| **Total area in hectares** | **19,091** |

*Uses:*
Due to its natural durability, lack of sapwood and ease of cleaving, chestnut is an incredibly versatile wood and it produces food.

Arbours
Barrels
Bird tables
Charcoal
Cladding
Decking
Fagots
Fencing posts
Firewood (wood burner)
Floorboards
Furniture
Gates / gate hurdles
Hop poles
Lath
Nesting boxes
Paling fencing
Pergolas
Post and rail fencing
Rose arches
Rustic furniture
Shingles
Steam bending
Timber framing
Trellis panels
Trugs
Walking sticks
Window frames
Woven panels
Yurts

Produces edible nuts, the flowers are a good nectar source for bees and it makes a good host for inoculation with the shiitake mushroom and chicken of the woods.

***Top: Frosted leaf of sweet chestnut.***

***Middle: Sweet chestnut cladding.***

***Bottom: Spiral growth is a common feature in older sweet chestnut.***

***Left: Billhooks from left to right: Yorkshire hedging hook, Old Elwell No.10, Knighton, Devon and Newtown.***

***Below: Flowers and seeds of the spindle tree.***

Timber is a heavy commodity to transport and is often moved thousands of miles by road and sea before it reaches its final destination, consuming a lot of fossil fuels on its journey. Coppice wood is truly sustainable. It is pruning on a grand scale. The trees are not killed; when cut they regenerate from the coppice more prolifically and begin at once growing their next yield. If cut and then processed in the woodland and marketed locally, the transport is minimised making this ancient form of woodland management the keystone upon which to plan our future timber yields.

I fell the five year old first; it is layed in drifts to ease the snedding process. One of the first lessons on arriving for training is the sharpening and maintenance of the billhook. During the cutting season the billhook is in constant use, the regular scratching sound of the sharpening stone across the blade is apparent at every tea break. By spring it is like an extension of your arm. There are many patterns of billhook and historical reasons and uses for the different shapes. I have a few old hooks but use primarily the 'Newtown' and 'Devon' patterns produced by Morris of Dunsford. These are modern hooks but made traditionally, they keep a good edge and at under £20 each, they are a fine investment. Once snedded, the poles are measured and graded into products. This is a difficult part of the process to learn, as poles that initially look similar are visibly different when you know what you are looking for. I cut template sticks and try not to introduce too many

products at once. It is easier to start with three choices of what the pole in your hand could be used for rather than twelve. It is a chicken and egg situation, once the apprentice has learnt to make a yurt, they know the tolerance in shape and can choose a trellis pole or roof rib with relative ease. But you can't make the yurt until you have graded the poles...

As the rain lashes down and the sticky Wealden clay pushes through the greensand to weigh down our boots, so the different piles of product begin to stack up.

To the south-east of the woodland, where the chestnut meets the grazing pastures I planted hedgerows back in 1990. The hedgerows are now well estab-lished, layed and successfully keep in a flock of sheep without additional fencing. In November they are a colourful spectacle with some of nature's hidden surprises like the vibrant colour clash of the berries of the spindle tree (*Euonymus europaeus*). The diversity in this hedgerow means a November walk is going to bring colour and of course I am here to harvest sloes from the blackthorn (*Prunus spinosa*). It is best to pick sloes after the first hard frost, then they can be made into wine or sloe gin. On account of their dryness I prefer to make gin which will make a fine drink after a frozen February day in the copse. Children cannot resist sloes and every time I pick them I too am tempted to pop that succulent looking little plum into my mouth. The result is a drying out of the mouth and an instant need for liquid. They are therefore best sweetened with sugar and turned into gin.

## Sloe Gin

Sloe berries should be picked after the first hard frost.

Take a 1 gallon demijohn and quarter fill with pricked sloes. Add ½ kilo caster sugar. Add gin until demijohn is half full. Put a cork in the top and shake vigorously. Shake demijohn daily until sugar has dissolved. After about two months, filter and bottle.

# NOVEMBER in Treswell Wood with Alistair Hayhurst

It is the beginning of November and I notice the days are getting shorter. By this time I would hope to be halfway through the coupes that I am coppicing for this winter.

I mainly work in Treswell Wood, owned by Nottinghamshire Wildlife Trust, a Site of Special Scientific Interest (SSSI). Of the 48.5 hectares, approximately 22 hectares are coppiced on a regular cycle. It was in Treswell where I started in the coppicing business. In 2000 I decided to set up my own business, Underwood Crafts, to initially supply hazel and willow hurdles and traditional coppice products and materials such as besoms, cleft gates and rustic furniture. This has developed over the years and I now also undertake hedgelaying, living willow structures, courses, demonstrations at country shows and most recently, yurt building.

I am back in Treswell Wood cutting the coupe I last cut seven years ago. The process of securing a coupe can be rather nerve-wracking. The previous spring, I received a letter detailing which areas would be coming up for cutting this winter. What I needed to do was to estimate the value and work out what I would be willing to pay. I then sent a letter to the Trust with my offer and waited... it's all based on a sealed bid system! Whoever puts in the highest bid gets the coupe.

When coppicing, I set up camp in the wood with permission of the Trust, both to lessen the commute and enjoy a few days in this gorgeous setting. Nowadays, unless I am cutting in late November, I can be sure that the leaf is still going to be on. This does not pose too much of a problem but if I left it to nature to help me in the process, I would not start cutting till early December. The coppice, primarily hazel and ash, is straighter and cleaner as a result of the standards being thinned out after a coupe has been cut. The compartment this year is now on its third cut; it was cut initially 14 years ago and the wood mainly went for charcoal with some hazel used for wattle hurdles. Prior to that, it was heavily cut between 1914 and 1918 for the 'war effort'. In 1938 another heavy felling of ash went for tool handles, axes and such like. Finally in 1958, again another 20 year interval, approximately 20,000 cubic feet was felled. Since the Wildlife Trust took ownership in 1973 the aim has been to maintain an ash-oak woodland in the form of coppice with standards.

The coupes work out to be about 0.3 hectare and this year the coupe has been divided between three of us. Once the area has been marked up, it

***Top: Alistair Hayhurst.***

***Left: Continuous willow hurdle.***

takes around a week to work my way through it. Working in Treswell is a joy. With the odd walker passing through and the volunteer work party coming in on Wednesdays, it's guaranteed that I get at least one visitor a day. The ground is fairly clear with very little bramble this year. Some years it seems I am fighting my way through it, but as the density of the stools increases, this tends to keep the bramble down.

When coppicing, I grade the rods as I cut them and the tops either go in windrows or are bundled for fagots. With ash poles, anything between 1-3 inches will go for hedging stakes and yurt poles. Naturally, the larger ones will be cleft down. Occasionally I discover an ash pole with a beautiful twist, the result of honeysuckle winding its way up it over time. This goes in the bundle destined for walking sticks. Ash of larger diameter, if it is straight and free of any knots, I keep for when I need a nice clean log for turning on the pole lathe.

One of the most pleasing aspects of being a coppice worker is that every piece of wood cut will have a use and waste is minimized. The material harvested, if it is not suitable for its traditional uses, is worked on and becomes a chair, coat hook or side table. Failing that, the wood heats my home and workshop, a resource I cherish.

Hazel is abundant in this coupe and, although there is the odd one which has naturally self-set, it mainly grows as a result of layering. When cutting the stool, one rod is left uncut which is later layered once all work in the coupe has been completed. To layer, the rod is bent over and the top is buried in the ground, this has been done almost each time a compartment has been cut in the last 14 years and the majority take root, producing fresh new hazel. As with the ash, I grade the hazel. Most of it will be made into hurdles but even then I like to bundle it in different grades. It makes it all a lot easier.

When back at the workshop and making the hurdles, I know where I can find the right rod for a particular job. Slender clean rods of good length will be used for binders in hedgelaying and any rods too big to be used in the hurdles are bundled, to be used in continuous fencing. I tend to do more of this type of work now for a variety of reasons. It involves the same principles as making a hurdle but as it is woven in situ, it can follow the contours and gradients of the land, lasts longer and the end result is a very neat and eye-pleasing fence. Furthermore, it gets me out of the workshop and I can also spend more time with customers discussing their ideas.

When not in the woods coppicing, November holds a rich mix of work. One of the most satisfying and rewarding is hedgelaying. This is a craft I was taught six years ago by Geoff Key, a national champion in hedgelaying. Geoff's infectious enthusiasm and passion for hedgelaying has rubbed off on me. I lay hedges in both Derbyshire and Midland styles using stakes and binders, where required, that I have brought out of the wood. A great feeling of satisfaction and achievement is often felt after a day's hedgelaying, transforming a large overgrown hedge into a stock-proof boundary. Hedgelaying provides an income in November as coppicing does not pay for itself until you have worked the material and transformed it into a product to sell, be it a wattle hurdle or yurt.

The techniques and touch that I learnt with hurdlemaking have contributed to my skill as a hedgelayer; where to make that initial cut, how the grain of the wood will run and knowing the wood's limitations.

Any rainy days are spent in the workshop. The woodburner is lit and with it being only a few weeks before Christmas, I build up stock for any Christmas shows that I am doing. This is work I particularly enjoy as it is varied, interesting and creative. Products range from Welsh frame baskets to Gypsy flowers and side tables to besom brooms.

***Left:***
***A 12 foot coppiced wood yurt.***

***Top right:***
***Carrying the hazel.***

***Bottom right:***

DECEMBER

# DECEMBER in Prickly Nut Wood

***Hedgelaying Midland style.***

It is a rare day that passes in my life where I am not lighting or tending a fire. I awake and expect the Rayburn to have kept in overnight. It runs purely on wood and cooks the dinner, heats the hot water and the house, running seven radiators, on two small wheelbarrows of wood a day. I put a 'keeper' log in the firebox last thing at night and most mornings there is a good bed of embers to start the day off. By first light, the fire will be well established in the outdoor kitchen hearth and the working day will begin there.

My apprentices soon learn the importance of fire in a woodsman's life. They heat their dwellings, cook all their meals and make every cup of tea with it. Then there are the brash fires in the wood. Unless I have a fagot order to complete, or a brash hedge to construct when the brash takes on a new level of value, most of the brash (lop and top) is burnt as we work through the woods. This may seem wasteful or unnecessary, but when you work in the woods and come back to recoppice an area where the brash has been left on the ground, it is a time consuming process making the woodland safe for felling again. Fire sites can disturb the ecological balance of very sensitive woodlands, so it is important to assess the woodland properly and make choices regarding fire sites and the number of them on a woodland-by-woodland basis. As well as clearing the brash, these fires are a companion during the winter months. They keep the kettle boiled, bake potatoes for lunch and warm hands that have been handling icy poles.

Brash fires are built on a pyre. Stems of standing dead wood are felled and crosscut to form a pyre on top of which the fire is built. Standing dead wood will supply dry wood even when it is raining. The ground is wet and damp in winter. A fire lit directly on it will be sucked by the damp soil below. The pyre allows the fire to start above the ground on top of the dry dead wood. By the time the pyre has burnt away, the heat has dried the damp ground beneath and the fire has a good heart within it and will continue to burn well.

Throughout the woodland are numerous assistants to the fire maker. For kindling there is the flammable bark of the silver birch (*Betula pendula*) and in season the fluffy seeds of goat willow (*Salix caprea*) which when dried have a similar texture to cotton wool. 'Cramp balls' or 'King Alfred's cakes' (*Daldinia concentrica*) burn as if they are charcoal and can play a useful role in fire lighting. As a woodsman it becomes second nature to collect these 'helpers' as you come across them in the woods. Feathering sticks is another useful tip which helps increase the surface area of kindling by exposing thin strands of wood. Start small and build it up gradually, many mistakes are made by starting with too big a fire and not allowing the fire time to build. Treat your fire as a living entity and nurture it. A fire needs food (sticks) and oxygen (air) to grow.

The fire in my outdoor kitchen has been lit almost every day for sixteen years. It has boiled thousands of gallons of water and fed many people. It has also been a place of meetings and stories. People from all around the globe have stared into the red embers recounting a tale or contemplating life, sung songs

*December title page: Using the flammable bark of silver birch to light a fire.*

*Below left: Rayburn at Prickly Nut Wood.*

*Above: 'King Alfred's cakes'.*

| Drying Times For Firewood | | |
|---|---|---|
| *Ready to burn 12 months after felling* | *Ready to burn 18 months after felling* | *Ready to burn 24 months after felling* |
| Birch | Beech | Oak |
| Alder | Hornbeam | Sweet chestnut * |
| Ash | Apple | Holly |
| Lime | Pear | Yew |
| Field maple | Cherry | |
| Sycamore | Hazel | |
| | Hawthorn | |

* Sweet chestnut can spit on an open fire, so best saved for the woodburner.

Coniferous softwood logs tend to spit and can contain high levels of resin but if that is what you have, then used in a woodburner in conjunction with hardwoods they will keep you warm over winter.

# Firewood

The majority of mixed coppice woodlands were originally fuel woods and many still are. Although wood as fuel has seen a decline, the increased costs and uncertain reliance on fossil fuelled heating shows that the local renewable source of wood fired power stations, if small and localised, is on the increase.

To the woodsman firewood is a necessity for warmth but also for a useful income during the coppicing season, when a lot of time is spent felling the materials for the summer's craftwork. Firewood needs to be properly seasoned. 'But ash burns green' I hear you say. Yes, ash will burn green but as a last resort. Seasoned wood burns best and seasoned ash is fine firewood.

For the coppice worker, wood cut for firewood usually needs to be seasoned near the ride in the woodland itself. Stacked well, and preferably covered on top but not the sides, the wind and sun will start the seasoning process. Once cross cut and split into finished logs, the seasoning will be quicker. The smaller size the wood is reduced too, the faster it will dry out and season. Different woods dry out at different speeds. *See Drying Times For Firewood table above.*

Most firewood producers have a processor or log splitter, which is either powered by an engine or tractor PTO (power take off unit) and splits the logs to the desired size. I still use an axe. For me, splitting firewood with an axe is a timeless activity, peaceful and satisfying, and it will soon warm you up on a cold winter's day. There is skill to splitting logs by hand: Reading the log by looking for knots or uneven grain; knowing when and where to split off sections before splitting across the diameter; and using the weight of the log to do the splitting by inverting the axe. I take pride in sourcing, cutting, seasoning, and splitting all the firewood I need to keep my family warm through winter. On this clear December day with the buzzards soaring overhead and a robin waiting eagerly nearby for insects as I work through the log pile, it is easy to feel at peace with the world.

December is often busy for logs as even occasional fire users want logs over the seasonal holiday whether celebrating Christmas, winter solstice or the end of a calendar year. In the woods we stop coppicing for a seasonal break on the winter solstice as the passing of the shortest day is an important event when you work on the land. It is time to gather in the colour of winter. A Christmas tree, holly, ivy, mistletoe, rosehips, fir cones and the hairy seed pods of wild clematis – old man's beard. It is a time to rest, take stock, celebrate, enjoy company and prepare for the rest of winter, most of it lying ahead.

*Far left:*
*Mistletoe berries, popular for a festive kiss and a useful part of a woodsman's winter greenery sales.*

*Left:*
*Lime is a good host tree for mistletoe.*

*Bottom left:*
*Rumford fireplace at the woodland house.*

*Bottom right:*
*Storm kettle.*

and shared laughter. It is enclosed within a circular brick hearth and has a high roof above to allow smoke to escape but keep the rain out. Kettles are boiled every morning and thermos flasks of hot water are filled that are then consumed throughout the day. In my twenty's I travelled in the Himalayas. In the mountain regions of Nepal and Tibet, I regularly met people carrying their thermos of hot water as they went about their day. What a saving on resources it would be if everyone kept one by their kettle and filled it each time the kettle was boiled. An electric kettle's heating element uses one kilowatt of power to boil it. A flask can reduce the number of times the kettle is boiled by 70%. The storm kettle (also known as the Kelly kettle) is in regular use when we are cutting coppice deep in the woods or out on contract laying a hedge or weaving a fence. A clever but simple design it allows the water to be boiled rapidly by using only very small sticks in very windy conditions. Designed originally for fisherman, it has deservedly become known as the fastest boil in the woods.

So first the Rayburn, then the outdoor kitchen fire, brash fire, storm kettle and then if it's a sub-zero winter night, I will light the open fire in the woodland house. Based on the heat efficient designs of Count Rumford it is economic on wood and very efficient in radiating heat and the perfect place to relax after a physical day in the coppice. Then of course there are the charcoal fires and the fires for steam bending. The relationship of understanding and respect of fire is paramount in the woodsman's life.

As I sned the poles, I am noticing quite a lot of grey squirrel damage, another reminder of the constant vigilance needed to keep the population of squirrels in

## Holly (*Ilex aquifolium*)

Evergreen native tree with distinctive red berries on the female tree.

*Growing conditions*:
Preference for acid soils but will also grow on limestone soils.

*Silvicultural practice*:
Slow growing evergreen native commonly found as an understorey species in oak and beech woodland. Traditionally left as a boundary tree and used in hedging. Used as fodder in wood pastures, with the current lack of grazing many of these pastures are seeing holly becoming a canopy species. Coppices well. A few ancient holly woods occur – these are a speciality in the British Isles and are a globally rare example of cool temperate broadleaved evergreen forest.

*Uses*:
Carving
Firewood
Horse whips
Inlay work
Machinery cogs
Mauls and mallets
Morris dancers' staves
Planks – ivory coloured timber, heavy in weight, fine texture and irregular grain
Posts
Pulpwood/board wood
Turnery
Winter fodder for livestock
Wreaths and Christmas greenery

***Top: Berries of the female holly, an important foliage product for the woodsman.***

***Middle: Coppiced holly at Prickly Nut Wood.***

***Bottom: A gnarly piece of holly makes a fine maul for striking a chisel.***

balance. The grey squirrel is an introduction that has thrived in British woodlands. Breeding rapidly and with no natural predators, it has pushed the native red squirrel into decline. With its tendency to strip the bark from trees, it has damaged numerous small trees and turned potential high value timber into firewood. The Forestry Commission have been involved in different attempts to control its popu-lation including, in the past, a 'bounty' where squirrel tails could be exchanged for a shilling at post offices. Present discussions on its control include the idea of feeding the squirrels contraceptives. Personally I think this would be a short-sighted idea as the risk of other animals accessing the contraceptives would be too high and it would contaminate a very good source of wild food. I won't use poisons so I have to control grey squirrels by shooting and trapping. In the sweet chestnut coppice at Prickly Nut Wood, the grey squirrels tend to attack the trees after they have established between three to seven years of regrowth since the previous cut. This is particularly frustrating as once the coppice has grown beyond the reach of browsing deer, it is easy to relax and think all is well. The grey squirrel strips the bark predominantly between July and September searching for the sugars contained within in sap. This is a time of year when the leaf is dense upon the trees and the grey squirrels can go about their bark stripping well hidden from the busy woodsman. The extent of the damage is not noticed until leaf fall.

If I am to kill an animal, then I will use the meat, so grey squirrel has become part of my diet. My apprentices soon get a taste for it and it has become referred to as 'bush meat'. I shoot with a .22 air rifle. Mine is an old classic, the Weihrauch HW35. The air rifle is a quiet weapon and a shot does not clear the woodland of every other animal in the vicinity, as a shotgun tends to do. Its ammunition is small and cheap and it also ensures the meat is undamaged. A shotgun is not so selective. Grey squirrels are clever and not the easiest of animals to shoot. In a large tree they will search out a thick branch and cling to the topside of it, often revealing no more than the tip of their tail. On a smaller tree they will always move to the opposite side of the tree from where you are standing, so having two people and two air rifles makes for more successful

hunting. Oily, my lurcher, is a great addition to any such outing as she is a trained squirrel dog. Grey squirrels are her prey and her mouth and nose show the scars and puncture holes of learning her trade. She catches many on the ground as they run but most importantly she points them. If she sights a squirrel in a tree, she will stand motionless at the foot of the tree, her eyes focused intently on the exact location of the grey squirrel. If I am not nearby she will bark. It is a particular sound that I immediately recognise as her squirrel bark, and when possible I will come to her call and shoot the squirrel. I only shoot during the winter months, when the leaf is off the trees. I also use 'lofting poles' to dismantle drays (squirrel nests) and encourage them to move on.

In summer you have little chance of finding a squirrel amongst the dense foliage of a chestnut wood so it is then I turn to a few traps. Trapping an animal involves thinking like the animal, understanding its habits and feeding patterns and then using an appropriate humane trap. Grey squirrels have favourite areas and I know from living in the woods where will be the most suitable place to set a trap. I use two traps for squirrels; the first is a cage trap. This is set on the ground and catches the squirrel live. There is a risk in the woods of catching weasels, which play an important role in rabbit control, so the cage trap ensures they can be released unharmed. All traps must be checked at least twice daily and more often in summer. The cage trap should be placed on the ground and carefully camouflaged with leaves and twigs and left baited but unset for at least a week. This encourages the grey squirrels to see it as a feeding station and they become used to visiting it. I usually bait the trap with nuts or peanut butter, but chocolate is also popular. Once a squirrel is caught, it is cleanly dispatched with the air rifle and

***Far left: Squirrel damaged coppice.***

***Left: Weihrauch HW35 showing the results of a good day's squirrel control.***

***Below left: Concentration – Oily's eyes never leave the squirrel.***

***Below: My brother, Dan, removing a dray with lofting poles.***

# Bush Meat Casserole

I offered this to BBC 'Countryfile' presenter John Craven when they came to film at Prickly Nut Wood. Disappointingly he was concerned that it might offend some viewers if he was filmed eating it, but he ate and spoke very highly of it off camera!

*Preparation*:
Grey squirrels should be gutted and skinned soon after killing. Turn the squirrel on its back and make an incision from the breastbone downwards. Remove stomach, intestines and offal and then cut the squirrel in two below the front legs. I give the head and front legs to my dog (after all it is usually her who guarantees we find the bush meat). Pull the skin downwards towards the back legs, this can be tough and small cuts with a knife between the skin and the flesh can help ease the process. Cut off the back feet and push the back legs through the skin. You are left with the two back legs and the saddle. For this recipe allow one squirrel per person and joint so that the back legs and saddle are separated into three pieces of meat.

*To feed four*:
Four grey squirrels prepared as above. Place a large cast iron pan on the fire and caramelise an onion in olive oil. Add squirrel portions and sear for two minutes, then place in pot and add marinade. Cover and leave for 24 hours.

*For the marinade*:
½ pint olive oil
4 cloves garlic (halved)
4 leaves chopped sage
Handful of fresh thyme
½ bottle of elderberry wine (or Merlot)

*For the casserole*:
Olive oil
2 onions
Selection of root vegetables cut into cubes:
- Potatoes
- Swede *
- Turnip
- Jerusalem artichokes
- Carrot
- Celeriac

2 bay leaves
1 tablespoon yeast extract
½ cup of pearl barley
Water

Gently fry onions in olive oil, add squirrel portions fry for a couple of minutes and leave to marinade for 12 hours. Add water to cover meat and slowly bring to the boil. Dissolve yeast extract and stir in root vegetables. Add more water, pearl barley and bring to the boil. Boil for a few minutes then remove from heat and place in Rayburn bottom oven (or slow cooker for at least four hours). Serve in a bowl with crusty bread.

* Swede can be very slow to soften and this recipe is improved if the swede is pre-boiled.

Controlling and eating grey squirrel is so much part of woodland life that I felt another recipe is necessary. This one is quick, delicious and a great way of introducing people to eating squirrel.

prepared for dinner.

The other trap I use is the Canadian Kania trap. This is a spring trap approved by Parliament under the Spring Traps Approval Act on 1st March 1993. It is a powerful spring trap which is set in the tree to reduce the risk of catching animals other than grey squirrels. The power of the spring causes an instant dispatch of the squirrel. The same procedure for the cage traps applies. Choose your site carefully, and then leave it unset as a feeding station prior to setting the trap. These two traps can help keep the numbers in control during the summer period as well as provide a regular source of bush meat.

I am not trying to eradicate grey squirrels from the woodland, just keeping the numbers in balance so that the damage they cause does not have a significant bearing on my livelihood. My control of grey squirrels is supported by Natural England (the government body for nature conservation) as part of the management objectives for Prickly Nut Wood, a Site of Special Scientific Interest.

## Party Squirrel

Choose a young squirrel and prepare the meat as for the casserole.

Take a sharp filleting knife and slice thin strips of squirrel from back legs and saddle.

Heat a large frying pan with olive oil and crushed garlic and briefly fry thin strips.

Remove and lay on absorbent paper to remove excess oil.

Place each piece of meat on a cocktail stick between a piece of cheese and a grape and allow your eager 10 year old son to distribute amongst unsuspecting guests at a party. Guaranteed reaction, mostly positive.

Grey squirrels are also very under-estimated meat. Commonly referred to as 'tree rats', the grey squirrel has not been well advertised as a food product. Hugh Fearnley-Whittingstall describes a forward thinking restaurateur who places grey squirrel on the menu as flightless partridge, and goes on to justify the name based on the quality of squirrel meat. This is the kind of good sense marketing that would see us enriched with the pleasure of a flavoursome new meat as well as helping the growth of our forests. A grey squirrel's diet is predominantly nuts, berries, wild mushrooms, tree sap and birds' eggs. No vaccines or antibiotics here.

How to cook grey squirrel depends upon their age. Young tender squirrels in their first year can go straight on the charcoal barbecue but once older, a slow cooked casserole is the best way to tenderise the meat. By December they are putting on a little winter fat and the best way of ageing is by size and condition of teeth. If in doubt this casserole recipe will ensure delicious tender meat whether young or old.

# DECEMBER in a Chiltern Beech Wood with Frankie Woodgate

In these days of 'must go', 'must move', 'must make', it's all too often overlooked, that until quite recently all the moving and making, going and taking was achieved in alliance with Messrs Horse, Pony and Ox! Our industrial and political heritage owes a great deal to the strength and endeavours of draught animals. From the front lines of grisly wars, the cultivation of land, the transport of coal from the dusty depths of mines, the hauling of timber from woods and forests and the general to'ing and fro'ing of people, these animals are intrinsically woven into the fabric of this land.

Some may regard the use of draught animals as antiquated. Now, though, with global and regional concerns about forest biodiversity, sustainable management and climate change, working horses are witness-ing a renaissance and have a firm hoof hold in the management of the natural resources that their predecessors helped to shape. So this is a 'horse logger's tale' – a day in the life of a professional woodswoman, her horses and a Chiltern beech wood.

December can give days cold and bright, with morning air sharp enough to take your breath away when you first step into the new day. A lattice of frosted leaves and twigs crunch beneath boot and hoof and a horse's warm breath creates tiny droplets of water vapour as I pass by a sky clad mix of elegant birches and rowans, rubbing shoulders with robust oaks and beech trees.

All very evocative and, on days such as this, December is at her benevolent best. The woods are alive with sounds of birds busying themselves amongst the beech mast and the 'hallooing' of dog walkers as they call their errant charges. Often these walkers will stop and remark 'what a wonderful sight', or 'How quaint, what a lovely life you must have working with these gentle giants'.

In part, they are right, it is a wonderful sight to see and I am glad that their walk has been embellished by the presence of my two heavyweight comrades. Strangely, however, when December throws her gauntlet down, the rain hits side-on fuelled by a northerly gale and I can no longer feel my fingers through sodden gloves, those friendly walking folk with their musings on the quaintness of my rural life are nowhere to be seen.

On these tempestuous days, various things continue to inspire me. The unfaltering generosity of my horses; that each day they are remarkable and that with a word (and a good breakfast) they will work willingly through the worst of winter weather. Ours is a working partnership based upon mutual trust. Whilst these so-called 'gentle giants' were bred to have a temperament fit for work, it is also true

***Above: Team shot – Frankie with Jeton and Yser.***

***Left: Rearguard at the horseline. From left: Clyde, Drum, Yser and Jeton.***

***Right: The commute to work, the cattle beyond are the only other traffic.***

to say that it is sound training and deft handling that helps to sustain a gentle natured horse. It can take years to make a good horse but in unsympathetic hands, just five minutes to ruin one! A forestry horse needs to be calm and steady, so too does its handler! Another thought, one of my father's favourite sayings, perhaps more practical than inspirational, flits through my mind: "There's no such thing as bad weather, just the wrong clothes!"... I quietly remind myself to buy a better pair of gloves!

December finds the 'Natural Traction' team encamped in the Chilterns working for the Woodland Trust. The team consists of my two Ardennes horses, Jeton and Yser, a collie dog named Boo and me, a weathered, mid-vintage Wealden woods-woman. With my lorry serving as mobile home, harness room and food store we are a self contained band of woodlanders and are able to live on site for several months at a time if the job requires...

The 'prop forwards' of the draft breeds, the Ardennes, are short, very muscular animals, still much used on the continent for both farming and forestry. The Ardennes lads are aided and abetted in their travails by Clyde and Drum, a pair of svelt, 18-hand Clydesdales belonging to my colleague, fellow professional horse logger and woodsman, John Bunce.

Our December working day begins at 5.45am. I light the lamp, turn on the radio for the weather forecast and stoke up the wood burner to boil the kettle for the elixir that is tea with honey. As I wait for the kettle to boil I make up the horses feeds for the day and hang their bridles by the stove to warm up the bits. When it's minus five outside, to my mind the last thing a horse needs is a freezing piece of metal putting in its mouth! They have three good feeds a day, the largest in the morning so that they have plenty of slow release energy (three shredded wheat is nothing to an Ardennes), a lighter lunch which goes in their nose bags ready to be taken into work, and an evening feed on our return.

With feeds prepared and tea brewing, I don my head torch (technology has bestowed us with some useful things) and with the mighty 'bark' of a tiny muntjac buck rattling the still of early morning, I set out with dog at heel, to where the horses are paddocked.

They are waiting for us, four huge heads

caught in the torchlight, peering expectantly over the gate. We lead them in, tie them to the 'horse line' and give them their feeds.

As they eat, I fuel up too and make sure that we have all that we need for the day, checking any equipment and harness that we need is in good fettle. Once fed, the horses are groomed, harnessed and with nose bags slung across the hames, we begin our journey into our wooded work place. Depending how far the work site is, I may ride one horse whilst leading the other, or if we need the forwarder that day, the horses are hitched in as a pair and I drive them from the footplate. You can keep the M25 and road rage; by horse and through the woods is the only way to commute!

The wood is a 'Plantation on an Ancient Woodland Site' (*PAWS – see June chapter*) and we are here for two months. We have worked this wood with horses for the past six years and spend anything up to three months at a time living on site and working a six-day week. We do the felling as well and are gradually thinning out the mixed conifer crop to favour any existing broadleaves and encourage natural regeneration. All the felled timber is then extracted by the horses using a range of purpose built equipment.

There are two types of management prescriptions that are employed on this site, both of which lend themselves perfectly to the use of horses. The first is a systematic thinning of the conifer crop; in this instance we remove one line in four, thereby reducing the conifer cover and benefiting the remaining crop. The use of horses for extraction also allows for the retention of any sound broadleaves emerging in the row. This is only possible because of the unparalleled manoeuvrability of the horses, which allows them to step sideways around any retained trees.

The second is the selective felling of conifers in a strip along the edge where the compartment borders a well established mix of broadleaf trees and 'halo' thinning to release existing hardwoods. We are careful to remove trees that would give a gradual change in light levels, deter invasion by bracken 'in waiting' yet provide open space for the broadleaves to seed into. Selective felling poses the question: "How do you reach scattered timber, surrounded by huge Corsican pine, delicate broadleaf regeneration and mature hardwoods without a defined extraction route?"

The answer is to use the traditional method of draught bar and traces also known as 'long gears'. Beautiful in its simplicity, this highly versatile, quick and

fficient system afforded the horse and andler ease of movement through the emaining crop, without incurring any amage to emerging broadleaves.

With long gears all we need is 3 feet learance, and we alternate our routes mongst the trees, reach the chosen timber, itch it to the draught bar and skid it to n area where we can pick it up with the orwarder. Skidding also provides a light carification of the soil, which produces a ood seed bed for any natural regeneration.

As an ancient woodland site, horse rawn extraction was employed not only or silvicultural reasons. The site's ecology nd evidence of archaeological features equire a low impact approach to forestry operations. Also, the tranquillity afforded by living rather than mechanised horse power is much appreciated by the wood's walking folk.

As only one horse from each team was required to work in this area, I am able to split the day's labours between Jeton and Yser. This 'job share' approach suits my veteran lad Jeton. A consummate professional, he's worked in the woods for 12 years, extracted several thousand tons of timber and at the venerable age of 16 is reaping the benefits of a younger horse joining the team. Yser joined us two years ago. Now six years old and fully trained, he has the energy and enthusiasm of youth on his side, so the old boy can spend a little more time tethered to a tree contemplating his hay net.

After four days with two horses the area is cleared and we are left with several neat stacks of 3 metre Corsican pine at ride side. Time to bring on the forwarder!

"Whoa, lads," I tell Jeton and Yser and they quietly oblige. The track is narrow and a dog walker is approaching, so courtesy is a must and we stop to let him pass by. 'Caution Horses Working' signs are placed on all tracks and footpaths approaching the work area but actually encountering a pair of heavy horses on a walk still evokes a range of responses.

"Wow! It's a horse with a HiAb… wait till I tell me mates… I've seen it all now!", exclaims the man with the Rottweiler. He holds fast to his dog, which is leaving its mark on a rear tyre of my six wheeled

***op left: In the row with Drum and ser. Beyond, the retained broadleaf an just be seen.***

***elow left: Lunch break.***

***bove: Wagons roll.***

***ight: Yser and Jeton take five, whilst he timber is unloaded.***

wagon. Jeton and Yser stand calmly waiting for my next command and once man and dog have moved off a safe distance I release the brake and say, "walk on boys". The horses lean into their collars, step out together and the forwarder rolls smoothly on, with another 3½ ton load destined for the stack half a mile away.

***Left: Skidding timber through a stand of natural regeneration and standing conifer to stacks beyond.***

***Below: Homeward bound.***

Once there, the horses stand, whilst I operate the crane and unload the timber. The forwarder allows the team to extract over long distances, keeping timber clean and delivers an output of up to 30 tons per day on this site. John also works a similar unit, so with both teams working our output can reach well over 50 tons per day – low impact, high output.

Once unloaded, it's time for a rest and some lunch. The horses are given their nose bags and whilst they tuck in, I fetch them a bucket of water and myself a flask of tea.

After lunch it's back to work until 3.45 and then, with the wintery sun sinking fast, we head home. Travelling back, a red kite flies a lazy arc above us, curious to see our horse drawn convoy. We return with enough daylight to unhitch, unharness and give the horses a groom before their evening feed.

Once the horses have had their fill they are taken back to the paddock for the night. "Thanks lads," I say as they amble off to graze, roll and rest, ready for the next day. Their work may be done, but ours continues until all the harness and equipment is checked and stowed away and logs are cut for the wood stoves and the camp fire. With the chores done, hurricane lamps lit, a hearty stew simmering over the open fire and the moon now high above the

JANUARY

trees, we settle back and raise a glass to another winter's day well spent in the company of woods and horses.

The sight of the mighty oak below the house is at its best in midwinter. The beautifully formed branching shape stands out majestically against the bright frosty morning or an icy moonlit night.

I am always amazed how a tree of this size can hold up so many huge branches, literally tons of weight outstretched from the main stem. This tree I estimate to be around three hundred years of age. It is in its prime of life and has not started to show any signs of middle age die back in the upper branches.

One of the reasons for cutting coppice during the winter period is that 'the sap has gone down'. The lack of sap in the wood aids the drying out process and makes the timber less susceptible to insect attack. But does the sap really go down? There is always sap in the sapwood of the tree but during cold spells of winter the flow of sap from the roots up through the tree is at its least, hence the expression 'the sap has gone down'. In spring the sap will flow most strongly up through the sapwood to the buds and leaves. The tree

## Fruit Trees

Every culture of forest dwellers that I have heard of or encountered plant fruit trees near to their dwellings. This is the evolution of common sense. The fruit is close by to pick and eat and can more easily be observed for pest and diseases or in the tropics, raiding monkeys.

I have a good number of fruit trees around the house and in small clearings within the woodland and in January I prune the apples and pears, though not stone fruit which I prune in late summer to avoid silverleaf (*Stereum purpureum*) infection.

The majority of fruit trees are grafted onto a rootstock. The rootstock will determine the eventual size of the tree, how long it is likely to live and when it will start producing fruit. With apples, the variety of apple is grafted onto a chosen rootstock. So, for example, a Laxton Superb apple grafted on to an M26 rootstock would start producing apples after 2-3 years and would grow no higher than 10 feet (3 metres) and would only be short lived. If the Laxton Superb was grafted onto an M25 rootstock, I would pick the same apple but from a large 25 feet plus (7.5 metres) high tree which would live many years but might not start producing fruit for seven years after grafting.

Around the house and edging the vegetable garden, I have a variety of carefully trained apples on M26 dwarfing rootstock. Further away I have apples on the medium sized MM106 rootstock and beyond those apples on M25 rootstock, which will be there for others to enjoy after my time.

***Left: Spur pruned apple tree at Prickly Nut Wood.***

I prune my fruit trees, first removing any dead or diseased wood and then spur prune the previous year's growth. (Care must be taken with tip bearing apple varieties so as not to remove all the fruit bud.) I also tie down the branches to create a slightly weeping form. This enables easy picking but also slightly stresses the tree encouraging it to produce more fruit bud. I take pride in my fruit trees; they bring me a whole range of pleasure throughout the year. While pruning I enjoy their expanding girth and vigour, in particular the trees that I grafted myself, and with them there is an almost parent-like concern for their well being. Then when spring arrives they delight me with their tantalising blossom and the busy activities of bees and hoverflies. Afterwards, I watch fertilised fruit swelling on the branches. During summer I enjoy the cider I made from their apples the previous autumn and then it's picking time again. In abundant years I am boxing up apples to take to my local greengrocer.

grows outwards as new sapwood is created and in turn the original sapwood dries out and, with the help of natural tannins, it becomes heartwood, the dead part of the tree. The visual distinction between sapwood and heartwood can clearly be seen in oak and sweet chestnut, both of which contain large resources of tannic acid, a natural preservative that makes the heartwood so naturally durable.

With the arrival of January, I feel an urgency within me to get a move on with the coppicing, while being equally aware there are many other seasonal activities that need my attention.

I know I have potentially three months left in which to cut the coppice but springburst will arrive when it chooses and I must be ready. In front of us stands the bulk of the forty-one year old chestnut. The weather has been wild and unpredictable and the ground is becoming heavy underfoot. Each stem averages 50-60 foot in height and, with the diverse range of products we are making, there is much product sorting, marking, labelling and processing for every stem.

The largest coppice stems have a diameter of 14-16 inches and these are cross cut to lengths of 8 and 12 feet. These will later be milled on my mobile Lumbermate sawmill and converted to wany edge boards for cladding of buildings and larger boards for public footbridges and boardwalks. Slightly smaller stems with a diameter of 10-13 inches are cross cut into 10 feet lengths and then cleaved with steel wedges to form four quartered pieces, these will then be used as rails in post and rail fence construction. The posts to be used with the rails will either be 6-7 inch round chestnut posts or 5x4 inch sawn sweet chestnut posts. All these materials are readily available within the area we are coppicing. Smaller timber will be split for fencing stakes and clean 4-6 inch x 4 feet lengths will be split out for laths. There is a steady demand for riven chestnut lath, as many listed buildings are required to use it in plastering applications. Other orders for chestnut poles this year include pergola poles, roundwood building poles, poles for

***January title page: Snow adorns the Prickly Nut Wood oak.***

***Above: Part of the chestnut stand with woodland house in the background.***

# Fencing

Fencing is a constant need in both the countryside and urban areas. Well managed local woodlands, and in particular coppice woodlands, offer a wide range of poles for hand crafted fences that need no chemical treatments. The softer, more natural lines of these fences make them an attractive option for a garden screen or a break between fields or parkland. The main coppiced species for fencing are sweet chestnut and hazel and to a lesser extent willow, oak and ash. Sweet chestnut with its natural durability offers a whole range of fencing products from the standard fencing post for stock fencing through to cleft post and rail fencing. This is a vernacular style of fencing in Sussex used to edge and partition fields. The cleft rails follow the natural shape and contours of the tree giving a far more aesthetically pleasing fence compared to a sawn post and rail alternative. Cleft chestnut post and rail can be adapted to create many alternative and functional designs like the deer fence we constructed at Blackdown Park (see *middle right photo*). Another important chestnut fence is chestnut paling. Chestnut pales are cleaved out of coppiced chestnut and then secured with wire to form usually 10 metre bundles in a variety of heights. In recent years there has been demand for chestnut paling fencing as a visual deer fence so that birds like the capercaillie and black grouse don't get injured, as has been the case with pure wire deer fences. Sweet chestnut is regularly used to make up trellis panels and often combined with hazel to make attractive but durable woven fences.

Coppiced hazel can be split and woven to form an attractive fence. The traditional wattle hurdle originally made for penning sheep is a beautifully crafted coppice product where the ability to twist the fibres ensures that the split hazel can wrap around the outer zales (uprights) and come back on itself and continue weaving. Willow is also used to make woven hurdles and oak can be used cleft to make lath panels or split like chestnut to make rails. Ash is occasionally used as rails or like sweet chestnut made into gate hurdles, which can be used as fencing panels.

***All fencing in photographs from Prickly Nut Wood:***

***Top right: Cleft post and rail with diamonds for tree planting.***

***Middle right: Chestnut deer fence at Blackdown Park.***

***Bottom right: Rustic chestnut picket fence.***

***Below: Chestnut and hazel panels.***

***Bottom: Diamond lattice trellis panel.***

to be extracted once coppicing is completed. Other poles are moved often with the help of cant hooks or timber tongs. A cant hook enables the average person to seem to have the strength of three people. With a simple levering movement, large poles can be turned and moved into position. Timber tongs are used either to drag timber or, when used as a pair, to lift cordwood lengths to a stack. Using the tongs makes it unnecessary to bend over and wrap your arms around a log; instead it is possible to lift with a straight back just bending at the knees. This is essential practice for back preservation.

Between two oak standards, we have lashed a chestnut pole and tied a canvas awning to create a shelter where we process pales for chestnut paling fencing.

wattle fence frames, smaller 2-3 feet poles for trellis panels, poles for rustic furniture, poles for yurt construction and poles for firewood and charcoal. The cant is carpeted with poles. The brashwood has been snedded and converted to fagots or burnt. A selection of different markings have appeared on the base of the cross cut poles to indicate their final use and whether to extract now or later. As the apprentices come to know the system, more markings appear and the wide range of products that can be sourced from a chestnut coppice begin to become apparent.

With coppice poles of this size and weight a minimal amount of moving is a major consideration. The larger diameter poles for saw logs and for roundwood timber framing are left where they lie

***Above: Pete Randall moving chestnut with a cant hook.***

***Right: Dylan Walker dragging chestnut with timber tongs.***

This shelter has become the focal point of this season's coppicing and forms a welcome retreat on days of relentless rain. It is here that timbers already quartered by wedge cleaving are peeled and then cleaved further on a cleaving brake to form pales. Some finishing with a side axe is necessary before they are bundled up into 25s and sent off to be wired into finished fencing bundles.

As we reach the end of the month, over half the coppice is felled, but a lot of extraction and processing remains. It has been a wet and mild January, which has brought on an early flash of yellow across the common. Gorse (*Ulex europaeus*) can often be found in flower in late

***Above: Author cleaving pales.***

***Left: Author with bundle of 25 pales.***

# Hazel (*Corylus avellana*)

One of the first trees to recolonise Britain after the last ice age. Deciduous native broadleaf.

*Growing conditions*:
Favours fertile, well-drained calcareous soils but will also grow strongly on acid soils.

*Silvicultural practice*:
Coppice or coppice with standards (usually oak). 3,038 hectares of working hazel coppice in the census of 1979-1982.

***Top right: Hazel catkins on a January morning.***

***Middle: Wattle and daub at Prickly Nut Wood.***

***Bottom: Hazel filtering sunlight.***

*Uses*:
Barrel hoops
Baskets
Charcoal
Crates
Edible nut and leaves
Fagots
Firewood
Foliage for cattle fodder
Hedging binders / etherings
Hedging stakes
Hurdles
Lath
Pea sticks, bean poles
Rustic furniture
Thatching broches
Thatching spars
Walking sticks
Wattle and daub

## Gorse Flower Wine

This is a wine well worth the painful process of extracting the flowers from between the thorns. I find it easier to cut shoots of flowering gorse and take them home where I can gradually remove the flowers in comfort in front of the fire.

At least ½ gallon gorse flowers
1kg sugar
3 lemons
White wine yeast
1 gallon water

Wrap the flowers in muslin (or an old net curtain) and simmer in the water for 20 minutes. Lift out flowers, squeeze and then return to the water still in the muslin bag. Dissolve the sugar and add juice and zest of lemons. Allow to cool until luke warm and add yeast. Cover with a cloth and leave in fermenting bin for three days stirring occasionally. Strain into demijohns, fit airlock and leave to ferment. Rack once wine begins to clear and bottle once fermentation ceases. Should be ready to drink by late August.

***Above: Gorse flowers harvested for wine.***

## Rabbits

Rabbits can cause a lot of destruction in woodland, especially to coppice regrowth if their numbers are not kept in check. So January is the ferreting season at Prickly Nut Wood and we net and ferret the burrows to bring the numbers into balance before they start breeding. Those of you who have seen an area of hazel copse grazed till it dies by lack of rabbit control will understand the importance of keeping the population at a balanced level. In the past we ate more rabbit and other wild meat. There was not the easy supermarket purchase option available, so we controlled rabbits and other predators of our coppice regrowth with more focused attention than many of us do now. Ferreting in the woods always seems fair hunting to me. It is rare that you find every bolt hole when netting a bury (rabbit warren), so the rabbit has a chance of escape. The rabbit bolts out of a hole to evade the ferret and then is caught in a purse net (works like a draw string bag). The rabbit is then humanely dispatched. This process has to be the best method for producing meat that is in good condition as the rabbit contains no gunshot.

***Above: Ferret entering a bury.***

## Rabbit in Cider

To prepare the rabbit follow directions for preparing squirrel. Rabbit is easier to prepare than squirrel as the skin comes away quite easily.

I rabbit (jointed)
2 onions
I clove garlic
I pint real cider
2 rashes streaky bacon
Olive oil
I bulb celeriac
2 carrots
½ swede
2 leeks
6 medium potatoes
Dessert spoon of mustard
Salt and pepper
Teaspoon of thyme
½ teaspoon of parsley
Bay leaf

Take a large casserole dish and fry onion and garlic in olive oil. Gently fry rabbit portions, add chopped bacon and then add cider, seasoning, herbs and bring to the boil. Simmer and add vegetables, topping up with water or stock to ensure sauce covers the meat and vegetables. Stir in mustard and transfer to oven I80°C for one hour before slow cooking in warm oven if you have a Rayburn or low heat oven if not. Slow cook for three or more hours.

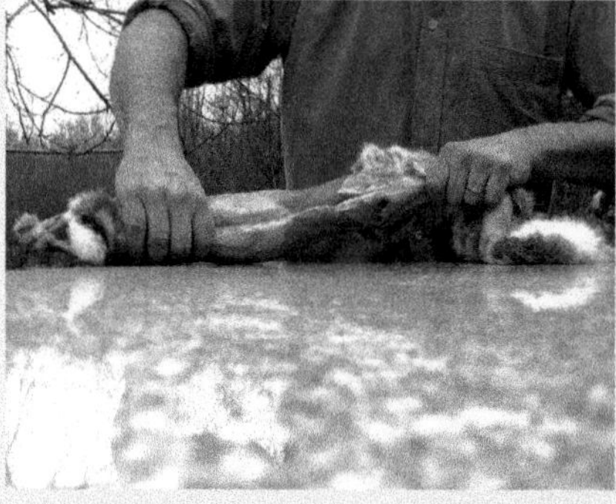

***Top: Skinning the rabbit.***

***Bottom: A jointed rabbit.***

***Right: Celeriac overwinters in the garden at Prickly Nut Wood.***

# JANUARY in Pepper Wood with Peter Broadley

January and the delightful coconut perfume drifting across the landscape can be bottled for late summer drinking.

After the over indulgence of the festive period it is great to get back into the wood for a bit of hard graft. As well as forestry being my profession I am also an active member of Pepper Wood Community Woodland Group. Pepper Wood is a 134 acre ancient semi-natural woodland near Bromsgrove in Worcestershire, owned by the Woodland Trust. The wood is roughly divided into three areas. One area is managed as coppice with standards, being sub-divided into coupes that are worked on a regular cycle. A second area of the wood is managed as high forest, and a third area is classed as non-intervention and forms a contrasting picture to the other management strategies. The volunteer group undertakes the majority of the work that goes on in the wood.

The main job for the winter season is coppicing (which is thought to be the original management strategy for the whole wood and was reintroduced in the early '80s). This work is undertaken by the group using only hand tools. The group consists of between four and 12 people on a good day covering an age range from late teens to post retirement age. One of the benefits of working without chainsaws is that it is possible to see and hear the wildlife around you, whether that be robins setting up their territories for the coming season or just having a conversation with the person next to you. This being one of the pleasures of working with a diverse group of people that share an interest in woodlands, and cake. Coffee and cake breaks are a regular feature of the work party day.

The areas being coppiced contain a mixed range of species from the nice and easy to handle and use like hazel, through to thickets of blackthorn interlaced with dogrose and honeysuckle, which require some delicate manoeuvring and usually a joint effort. Most of the rods being cut are used as hedging stakes and binders as required by the local style of hedgelaying. Other products such as beanpoles, pea sticks, walking sticks or even besoms are made to order to further utilise the crop. Most years all of our produce is sold. Anything leftover is used for charcoal burning later in the year. All the money goes to finance the group activities, the group being self-sustaining as far as funding goes.

Other jobs include maintenance of the small pond we have in the wood. It was surveyed back in 2003 and found to contain all three types of newt, including a breeding population of great crested newts. It also holds various vigorous species of plant life including non-natives such as floating pennywort, which if left would overtake the whole pond making it difficult for the newts, frogs and other aquatic life to thrive. The work for two of us consists of one wading in with a

***Top: Peter Broadley.***

***Left: Milling site at Pepper Wood Community Woodland.***

***Above: Layering hazel to improve stool density.***

***Below left: One of the frequent coffee and cake breaks.***

***Below right: Bundles of pea sticks.***

***Opposite page: Chainsaw milling in action.***

rake and dragging the weed to the bank where it is pulled out and left for a week or two so that any creatures accidentally removed have a chance to return to the water. The weed is then bagged up and disposed of in the appropriate manner.

One day this activity had to be post-poned because a very young muntjac fawn had taken to sitting next to the pond, and it was decided not to disturb it. Muntjac in large numbers can be devastating to young plants, particularly coppice regrowth. As a result the areas that we coppice are fenced for two years after the cut until the growing tips are generally above browsing height. (The fencing we acquired second hand from a local Forestry Commission site from where it was being thrown away.) This method has proved extremely successful and so it has been decided that at present no other form of deer management is required. I think Pepper Wood has space for one more small deer however.

Another task is bird box maintenance. There are about 80 boxes looked after by two dedicated volunteers who are not particularly interested in grubbing about on their knees around the base of coppice stools. The main inhabitants are blue tits, although boxes for woodpeckers and owls have also been placed at appropriate locations as there is not yet much natural habitat for them because the bulk of the wood was clear felled just after the war, making the majority of the trees no older than 60 years.

A further income stream for the volunteer group is oak planking. The timber for this comes from areas in the high

forest that are cut to increase the age diversity of the wood. (A task I undertake earlier in the season in my professional capacity.) Most of the timber cut is sold as firewood, but anything of a great enough diameter is selected out and saved to be milled into planks.

This is achieved using a frame style chainsaw mill. As this is an extremely noisy and dusty job, it is done well away from where the coppicing is going on. The logs are processed next to the age diversity areas from where they came, which is one of the main advantages of using a portable mill. Only the milled and much easier to handle planks are moved away from the cutting area. We are also planning to buy a device to enable us to make square posts, thereby utilising the smaller diameter logs, planks and posts for a use more valuable than firewood.

When I get the opportunity I like to visit the wood on non-work party days just to walk around and enjoy the wood for its own sake. I feel that I see the wood from a different perspective, with new eyes if you will; coming to the wood with two different objectives. Being on my own and being quiet I get to see things I might not normally see, like adult muntjac amongst the brambles in the age diversity areas. The stools are protected by brash fences which from the observable regrowth are obviously effective. I have heard that muntjac like eating bramble leaves although I have never seen them browsing. Wandering around the different sections of the wood, I am able to witness the onset of the new season. Catkins open on the hazel and honeysuckle comes into leaf very early on in January. Later on, the first green shoots and leaves of plants like foxglove and bluebells poke through the leaf litter, along with the occasional splash of colour of scarlet elf cap fungi amongst the universally subdued browns of winter. And on the end of some broken birch twigs, three drops of sweet sap, a promising sign of future liquid enjoyment. The wood is definitely starting to awaken after the winter sleep.

The advantage of co-operating with a group of people with a common interest is that all of this can be shared and appreciated together. I think a good experience shared is an experience doubled (converse to the usual saying about problems). The more community groups there are the better. By their nature they are inclusive and sharing. Co-operating and sharing amongst a small group can lead on to sharing with

FEBRUARY

# FEBRUARY in Prickly Nut Wood

the wider community, which can only be a good thing. In conclusion, I can rarely think of a better or more fulfilling way of spending a Sunday than going to the woods. At one time in the village of Lodsworth where I live, there was a wonderfully productive cobnut orchard. The majority of it has disappeared but remnants can be found at the bottom of some of the village gardens. One small area of about half an acre remains intact. I first cut it about eight years ago when the regrowth was very overstood and each stem averaged about 4 inches in diameter. When visiting it last September I collected boxes of nuts and realised it was more than ready to cut again.

Cobnuts are the productive cultivar of the common hazel (*Corylus avellana*). Traditionally they are managed to form a goblet shape from the old growth and the new growth of shoots is then 'brutted', partially snapped and left bent down to encourage the formation of more fruit bud. I have not brutted this orchard as it is very productive with the stems growing straight and a good shake provides plenty of nuts. Also by allowing the growth to be straight, I can use the regrowth for hurdles, fencing panels, binders etc.

The rods are a bit more gnarly than common hazel but with the help of a small cleaving brake, we are successfully gathering and splitting a couple of thousand rods. This is a great learning curve for the apprentices. Having learnt to cleave large rails with wedges and pales with a froe, they are now cleaving hazel of only one inch diameter with a small hand adze. This is a lovely tool and a solid week of cleaving these rods should ensure the knowledge is well digested.

The rain is not letting up, but it is good to be out of the chestnut and enjoying the feel of a different wood. With the hazel split and bundled it is time to transport it 400 yards to where we weave it into chestnut frames. This is about as good as it gets regarding timber miles.

One trailer load of chestnut for the frames – distance travelled: ½ mile.

Two trailer loads of split hazel for the weave – distance travelled: 400 yards.

All the timber has been cut from coppice management systems and the end result is a fine fence.

It is a true privilege to wake up as I do on occasional winter mornings and look out upon a pristine white woodland. Untouched by humans the virgin snow reveals the tracks of other woodland inhabitants. Deer tracks stand out clearly and I follow them to find their secret lairs. The snow is hanging heavily on the branches and yesterday's brown muddy woodland

***February title page: Birches weeping with snow.***

***Above left: Cutting and processing the cobnut orchard. Richard Bates cleaving hazel with a small adze and a cleaving brake.***

***Top right: Coppice stools disappearing beneath the snow.***

***Far right: No work today!***

***Middle right: Roe deer tracks.***

***Bottom right: Frozen rosehips add colour to the whiteness.***

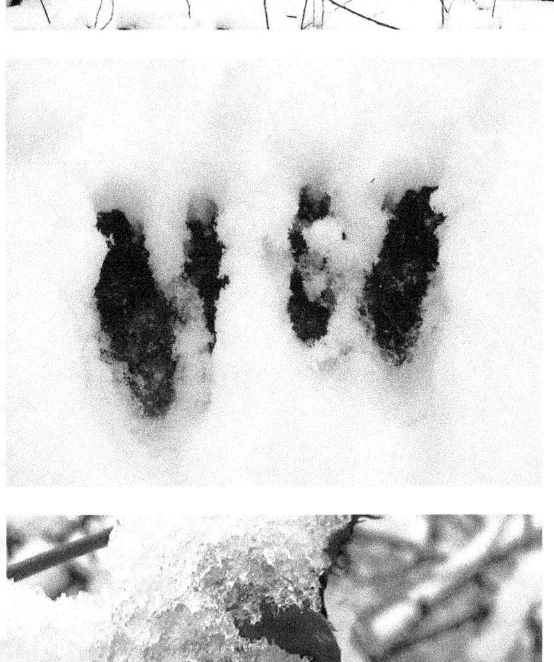

rides look fresh and enchanting. Ice frozen hazel catkins and the last remaining rosehips are colour amplified by their white surround. Birches weep to create snowy tunnels across the tracks and the poles I was cleaving yesterday have disappeared beneath the sparkling white carpet. No work today, snow only makes an occasional appearance in my woodland year and apart from a little tracking it is time for play. I wax the runners of the sledge and two excited children take a tour through 'Narnia' along the woodland rides.

## Deer

Deer can stand alongside grey squirrels as prime destroyers of woodland. Coppice regrowth is especially fine deer fodder. I am fortunate enough that sweet chestnut, being so full of tannins, is a little disagreeable to the deer's palate who see it as a food of last resort rather than a delicacy like hazel. Unless hazel is well deer fenced, regularly stalked, or preferably the coppice worker with a dog for scenting is living within the woodland, the hazel is likely to be eaten to the ground.

There is a larger population of deer in the UK than there has been for many years. I have roe and muntjac to contend with, others have sitka, fallow or red. As with all wildlife it is a question of numbers and balance. It is possible to keep the deer population controlled to numbers whereby the damage to the woodland is minimal but the remaining deer within it have a life free to roam. Controlling deer involves stalking. Deer stalking and the culling of deer by a marksman with a rifle is without doubt the most humane method of deer control and the legalities of the culling of deer are bound in legislation in the Deer Act of 1991. It is possible to take a course and train in deer stalking and apply for the appropriate firearms licence but it is often more sensible to employ a qualified stalker to control the deer population.

Venison is a prize woodland meat and I can offer no better start to the day than a recipe based upon Hugh Fearnley-Whittingstall's stalker's breakfast (*see below*).

## Stalker's Breakfast – Roe Liver

500g roe deer liver
50g unsalted butter
175-200g large field mushrooms, sliced
1 large red onion
a few sage leaves, chopped
small pot of soured cream
salt and freshly ground black pepper
toast or fried bread to serve

I have always had a bit of a love/hate relationship with liver. It probably comes from eating tough, over-cooked liver as a child at school. This recipe has cured me, the combination with sage is particularly fine.

Prepare the liver by removing any outer membrane and large tubes, then cutting it into thin strips. Heat half the butter in a heavy-based frying pan until it starts to foam (do not allow it to burn). Add the red onion and mushrooms and fry until they are nicely coloured and the water coming out of them has evaporated. Move the onions and mushrooms to one side of the frying pan, add the remaining butter and fry strips of liver for about three minutes, turning from time to time. Stir in soured cream and throw in the chopped sage for the last minute of cooking. Season with salt and pepper to taste, then pile the liver and mushrooms on to toast and serve at once.

## Herb Crumbed Saddle of Roe

Another venison recipe I am particularly fond of combines using steak strips from the saddle with breadcrumbs and herbs.

2lb roe deer steak
1 egg
1 lemon
3 tablespoons flour
2 cups dry breadcrumbs
Salt and pepper
1 teaspoon thyme
1 teaspoon wild marjoram
½ teaspoon tarragon

Cut the steak into small portions and beat to flatten it slightly. Beat the egg and add lemon juice, salt and pepper. Chop the fresh herbs and mix with the breadcrumbs. Dip the steak portions into the flour, then the egg mixture, then the breadcrumbs and herbs. Fry for a couple of minutes, turning regularly in olive oil or butter.

Serve with sauté potatoes, spring greens and mushroom gravy.

## Birch Sap Wine

Birch trees are best tapped usually late February to early March but it can be earlier depending on the winter. Pick a sunny day and choose a tree of at least 10 inches in diameter and with smooth not deep fissured bark. Tap the south side of the tree using a brace and bit. Choose a bit of equal diameter to the plastic pipe you are going to insert into the tree. A 12mm clear plastic pipe is good. Drill slowly into the tree in an upwards direction at about 45°. Go slowly as you only need to enter the tree by about ½ inch before the sap will start to flow. Insert the pipe into the hole and the other end into the demijohn. Cover where the pipe enters the demijohn with cotton wool or an old paper cup to deter wine flies. Leave for a few days and then collect sap. Remember to plug the drilled hole with wood or clay to stop the sap continuing to flow after you have taken your share.

1 gallon birch sap
2 lemons
½lb raisins
2lb sugar or 2 pints honey
Yeast

Squeeze lemons and add a little grated zest to the birch sap and boil for twenty minutes. Pour sap onto sugar or honey and chopped raisins. Stir until sugar or honey is dissolved. When luke warm add yeast and then cover with cloth and leave in fermenting bin until initial fermentation has slowed down. Then strain into a demijohn, top up with water as necessary and fit airlock. Should be ready to drink by late summer.

***Left: Tapping the birch.***

***Above: Early morning sun catches the sap collector.***

***Right: The frozen pond at Prickly Nut Wood.***

***Below: Woodland ride.***

The snow has come and gone and all around are signs of an early spring, buds are swelling and the sense of urgency sharpens within me. We will need to finish coppicing well before the end of March this year in order to extract and be away from the stools before they start to shoot again.

I hear the regular tapping of the great spotted woodpecker (*Dendrocopos major*) on the nuts outside the kitchen door. He is a regular visitor at least twice daily during the winter period when we offer the birds a little help. I sometimes question the wisdom in inviting a woodpecker to take food from a house made of wood with a wooden shingle roof. I hope that provided there are nuts to be had, he is less likely to feel the need to investigate the shingles!

Walking through the woods I see the elder (*Sambucus nigra*) has broken leaf. It is always early to show signs of spring, yet it can be deceptive as I have known it break into leaf and be followed by snow and cold weather. I notice the badgers have been having a clear out. Small heaps of bed litter and earth have been turned out. This is often a sign that young are present. The badger is a very clean animal and has a collection of latrines all of which are a fair distance from the set. Badger cubs that are confined underground will foul their bedding and the sow-badger will clean out the set regularly. Badgers are protected under the Protection of Badgers Act 1992. There are a number of badger sets within the woods and although I rarely see them, I occasionally come upon one on his night time errands while I am strolling back from a pint at the local.

The long tail tits are back, flitting through the birch trees, hanging on the catkins. Soon, like myself, their season will change and then they become master nest builders, often using up to two thousand feathers in their elaborate

## Birch, Downy (*Betula pubescens*)
## Birch, Silver (*Betula pendula*)

Historically the earliest native trees to colonise after the last ice age.

*Growing conditions:*
Likes most soils, downy birch can tolerate poorly drained soils.

*Silvicultural practice:*
Pioneer species of secondary woodland, coppices well when young and is commonly used as a nurse crop. Primary coloniser of heath land.

***Top right: Birch catkins.***

***Middle: Delicate branches of birch laden with snow.***

***Bottom: Birch bark.***

*Uses:*
Bark for canoes
Bark for fire lighting
Bark for furniture veneers
Besom brooms
Bobbins
Charcoal
Firewood
Furniture
Horse jumps
Internal flooring
Kitchen utensils
Mushroom log host for shiitake
Plywood
Pulpwood/boardwood
Sap for wine
Toys
Turnery
Veneers

# FEBRUARY in Pentiddy Woods with Ele & Anthony Waters

oval masterpieces. It makes one's own building skills seem very modest.

I am Ele Waters of Pentiddy Woods, a woodland and permaculture project on the edge of Bodmin Moor in Cornwall. My husband, Anthony, crafts greenwood furniture, manages local woodlands and runs courses through his business Heartwood Creations. I am a Forest School Leader and novice smallholder and home educate our two children, Elowen aged 5 and Adeon aged 3. Pentiddy has been home for us since 2004 when we received temporary permission to live here as resident woodsmen.

Pentiddy Woods is a relatively new venture – in fact incredibly young in terms of woodlands. The 27 acres of land were purchased in 2001 with 50% existing woodland. It is now 85% woodland, and we plan to achieve a final figure of 90% by 2009. Therefore we are far from experiencing an 'average' February. Implementation of the permaculture woodland design is the focus at the moment with a shift to ongoing management in a couple of years. Full productivity from the woodland is not expected for another 15-20 years.

February in any working woodland is a time of great contrast. Whilst much of the wildlife is fairly dormant, human input is at its greatest. There are however the first stirrings of the coming season: buds start to swell and spring bulbs begin to push upwards; bluebell leaves and the first snowdrop flowers bravely poke out through the leaf litter; the hazel catkins open to release their pollen on the cold winds in the hopes of finding the tiny hidden red flowers. Meanwhile, the robins and wrens become increasingly active, mistle and song thrushes proclaim their territories from the tree-tops, but the far-flung travellers such as the chiffchaff and swallow have yet to return. Many deer, foxes, badgers and rabbits are awaiting the birth of their young. If the month is particularly mild, the blackthorn treats us to some of the first flowers of the year. However, much of this activity is hidden and the woods are generally quiet. Amidst the dormancy we are in the throes of planting new coppice, harvesting timber, hedgelaying, felling and path creation, whilst watching eagerly for the first stirrings of life amongst the sleepy hibernation.

***Top: The Waters family.***

***Left: Alan Titchmarsh tries one of Anthony's benches at the Chelsea Flower Show.***

***Right: The female flowers of hazel often go unnoticed as the larger yellow catkins catch the eye.***

***Top right: Community tree planting.***

For the last six years our Februarys have been dedicated almost entirely to tree planting as we push to get the saplings in, and ideally mulched, before the sap starts to rise and the grass starts to gather strength. Nine acres of coppice are being planted, seven of which will be open to the public. It comprises coupes of sweet chestnut, ash, lime, hazel and mixed coppice. There are also plans for a woodland burial site and a roundhouse for educational and community use. We always gladly accept any help offered for the planting as it is a huge task given the rocky ground and the sheer quantity of trees (21,000 on completion). Community tree planting days are always great fun and a boost to our morale. Cheered on by a hearty winter soup, fresh cakes and samples of homebrew, the band of volunteers always do a great job (but noticeably achieve far more in the morning than the afternoon!). Community groups and businesses also contact us requesting the chance to get involved in the planting, e.g. the Scouts, local schools, countryside management students and those on team-building exercises, and of course we make good use of our WWOOFers (World Wide Opportunities on Organic Farms) at this time.

February is usually the time we prune the fantastically coloured willow around the site, including the children's willow 'monster'. We cut the rods into one foot lengths and plant them by pushing them into the ground to grow around the coppice. This forms a double row of willow around the edge as a sacrificial crop for the roe deer to fray against, willow being their preferred species. We also use the whole rods to create new living willow structures on and off site. The thinner of the remaining rods together with plants such as dogwood, bramble, holly, honeysuckle and ivy are harvested now for basketry. They are weathered under a hedge for a few weeks and then are woven into functional baskets to be used around the woodland holding.

With financial assistance from the Forestry Commission through the EWGS (English Woodland Grant Scheme), February 2008 will hopefully see work beginning in earnest in the existing mature woodland. This area has seen years of neglect and has been heavily browsed by cattle and deer. At present it consists of oak and beech over holly, hazel and gorse. We plan to fell beech, holly stands and gorse thickets where removal favours the growth of oak. This will help to redress the canopy composition and improve the quality of the invertebrate habitat. Regenerating areas of existing hazel coppice by removing yet more of the invasive species will also improve light penetration to the limited ground flora. We are creating new rides to link up the old charcoal platforms to enable the moving of the charcoal kiln and to allow for timber extraction up the steep slopes. The timber to be felled is mostly poor quality. Any decent timber is planked with our friend's mobile mill, whilst the remainder is seasoned for a year and then removed for firewood or converted into charcoal for sale in the local farm shop.

Working in the woods at this time of year, we are sometimes rewarded with sightings of deer as they become bolder in their struggle to find food. Wild food for us is also scarce – the occasional snack of a navelwort leaf gives us a promise of Springtime abundance, but hardly abates

management contracts to keep a trickle of money coming in. We also start to think about springtime work and any preparations that may need to take place. Timber is harvested from local woodlands and transported to the barn. Stara Community Woodland, 3 miles away, supplies us with windthrown Douglas fir for larger constructions. Small diameter sweet chestnut from the re-establishment of over-planted coppice is also harvested and used for furniture making. The bark of much of the chestnut is removed immediately after cutting and dried to be woven into seats for dining chairs and stools.

We have areas of woodland set aside for Forest School and bushcraft activities which are focused on having fun and learning despite the weather at this time of year. It is important for children to

the appetite! Young wild garlic leaves can be picked for salad but the main crop is yet to come. Rabbit and squirrel occasionally grace the table much to the delight of the children. If the month is particularly mild, the sap in the birches may begin to flow adequately to tap for wine and we bravely tackle the gorse patches for the much favoured gorse flower wine. Supplies of food collected in the Autumn such as hazelnuts and chestnuts dwindle, but our previous year's harvests from the elder trees come into their own in the season of colds and flu. Elder Rob, a syrup of elderberries, ginger and cloves, soothes throats and coughs whilst elderflower tea reduces fevers and catarrh. The wine from the berries somehow seems to make every ailment disappear (at least temporarily!).

Working on our own land does not yet give us a direct income, so interspersed with the work at Pentiddy is occasional offsite work such as hedgelaying and various woodland

## Elder Rob

I'm not sure where I got this from but it's a good old traditional one!

Elderberries
Cloves
Demerara sugar
Root ginger

Place prepared fruit in an ovenproof dish and crush well to extract the juice. Put in a cool oven for 45 minutes. Strain through muslin. To each pint of juice add 1lb of demerara sugar. Put well bruised root ginger and four cloves into some muslin and simmer all together for 30 minutes, stirring until the sugar is dissolved. Remove spices after 15 minutes. Strain and bottle when cold. To increase shelf-life, add a small amount of brandy before bottling.

*To drink*:
Dilute 1 tablespoon in a glass of hot water.

*For coughs*:
Dilute 2 tablespoons with 1 tablespoon honey in a glass of hot water.

learn how to stay warm in the woods in winter, so games and activities tend to be energetic and dynamic or involve fire. There are many elements to firecraft which we give children the opportunity to explore safely and which we practice ourselves at our informal bushcraft gatherings. The group shelters also come into their own as we sit around the fire cooking stews and telling stories. The plentiful mud and occasional snows of February offer fantastic opportunities for tracking animals and learning more about their activities. Children engage wholeheartedly in looking for tracks and the first signs of spring and appear to sense the anticipation in the earth around them. Activities such as putting out nesting material for the birds that includes coloured wool is great as the children have been known to find their offerings in a nest at a later date.

Back at our house, a cosily adapted mobile home on the edge of the woods, we celebrate Imbolc – the Celtic festival of awakening. It is a time to plant seeds for our future growth, look for new beginnings and new ways forward. If our off-grid water and power systems work as they should (which is not always the case!), we enjoy the dark, cold evenings and the daily lighting of the home fire. With daylight for outside work being limited, we sit around on the floor of the kitchen (the only warm room in the house) singing or whittling toys for the children. The musical instruments have a chance to provide entertainment after a days work rather than just gathering dust as they tend to in the summer.

Everything we have created here has been dictated by the nature of the land and its environs. It feels as if we have been led by the potential of the land itself, sometimes in unexpected directions. It certainly offers us years of varied work. It is rewarding to think that in Februarys in the future, surrounded by wildlife that has made this new habitat its

***Top left: Adeon helping chop wild garlic for a woodland soup.***

***Top right: Making popcorn with sieves.***

***Bottom right: The Waters' home at Pentiddy.***

MARCH

home, we will be coppicing and stacking timber for a multitude of uses from trees that we planted in Februarys past. Looking across the freshly coppiced woodland at the beginning of March, it is hard to remember how large an area it looked to cut back in November. And now it lies horizontal, snedded, motionless, awaiting extraction.

Extraction is an important part of woodland management, and if not done carefully, it will leave the woodland rutted and compacted, a sight that gives foresters a poor reputation. Small diameter coppice like in-cycle hazel can be bundled and carried out on the shoulder. The larger the timber cut the greater the visual impact on the woodland and rides. My aspect and soil type add to these challenges. Being on a clay soil and the north-east face of a hill, the rides are often wet and the need for regular repairs, drainage culverts and crushed stone all bite into the economics of managing the woodland. The woodland is a Site of Special Scientific Interest (SSSI) for its bryophyte community: mosses, lichens, liverworts and ferns which are mainly evident on the coppice stools. It is in my

***March title page: Sunrise behind the Prickly Nut Wood oak.***

***Below: Felled coppice awaiting extraction.***

The majority of coppice woodlands have some standard trees growing amongst the underwood. Standards make the optimum use of vertical space and give a high value return on top of the under-wood produce, as well as adding diversity and more habitat to the woodlands. The key is to get the right balance of standards per hectare and to try to have a varied age of standards throughout the coppice. Too many standards will over-shade the underwood and cause poor quality rods to grow on the coppice stools. One of the more traditional combinations is oak standards over hazel underwood.

Many coppice workers are not equipped to manage the standards. Because of this, they often get left until they grow too big and their crowns have overshaded the underwood and starved it of light and the coppice worker of his/her materials. The value of an oak butt is very poor when you consider how many years it has been growing and the energy used to fell, extract and transport it. This is where mobile sawmills are such an essential part of a small scale sustainable woodland management system. If the oak standard is felled and the limbs become cordwood, which in turn becomes firewood or charcoal, and the main trunk is milled up into planks, put into stick, air dried and then ten years later turned into two fine farmhouse dining tables – the woodsman will have very pleasingly added value to the oak butt and will have only had to transport planks on a trailer or roof rack rather than try to extract maybe over a tonne of oak butt.

Mobile sawmills can be hired with an operator for the day and this is a good way of converting standards if you only have a few each year. After many years of hiring, I purchased a 'Lumbermate' mobile mill a couple of years ago. This is a simple manual bandsaw mill and is at the budget end of mobile sawmills. It tows as a trailer and can be operated statically on the ground. Logs are rolled onto the bed with cant hooks, with the assistance of a winch if necessary. I have used it for milling all the timber for a green oak barn and it milled all the cladding, floor joists, roof rafters, floorboards for my workshop and house. I also have some good table planks air drying for the future – these are my pension.

I must mention here 'The Mule' developed from an American design by Cornish woodsman, Tino Rawnsley. Tino discovered the idea of the mule while researching solar drying kilns in the USA and now manufactures a model available in the UK. With the mule and its clever lever action I can lift up 5m long, 30cm butts and wheel them to my sawmill. This one tool has saved me many hours of struggle and has proved excellent in the movement of beams while timber framing.

***Above left: Oak standard amidst chestnut coppice.***

***Below: Author moving a larch butt with 'the mule' ready to be rolled onto the Lumbermate mobile sawmill.***

management agreement with Natural England that I cut the stools higher than would be normal silvicultural practice for coppiced sweet chestnut, so as to leave a larger surface area for bryophyte growth. Along with a dense stocking rate of sweet chestnut this makes for awkward terrain for extracting timber. Even horses can struggle to find a path between the high coppice stools in this landscape and I am looking at new extraction paths on the steeper slopes to favour horses for the future. But for this year it will be ropes, pulleys, winch and a vehicle. I have one main hard surfaced stone ride which runs above and to the north of the cant we have cut this year. By positioning my vehicle on the hard ride, I can use the ropes to slide the long poles over bearers to the ride edge where they can be further processed. This is an effective process that ensures the vehicle stays on the ride and does not enter the woodland terrain and compact the soil.

The extraction goes smoothly, a window of dry weather has made a huge difference and at last this season's coppicing is complete. The felling though is not quite over, there is a cluster of oak standards which will benefit from me felling two of them.

Mid-March and it is time for my first short course of the woodland year, 'mushroom inoculation'. The woods supply the woodsman with a diverse range of fungi throughout the year but none of it can be guaranteed to appear. By inoculating logs, there is still no guarantee but there is a very high probability that the woodsman can control the arrival and timing of mushrooms for eating and selling by using good rotational management of the log piles.

I have been inoculating logs with mushroom spawn for ten years, trialling different species of log and a few different varieties of mushroom. My most reliable inoculation has been the Japanese shiitake mushroom (strain: Adam) into sweet chestnut logs. Adam has also done well in oak, birch, alder and field maple. For the course I have selected 50 sweet chestnut logs about 45cm in length and 10-15cm diameter. The trailer is set up as a work bench and the first phase for the logs is drilling. I use a specialist Japanese drill bit to drill a large number of holes about 12cm apart across the whole log. Then using a brass inoculating tool it is possible to fill the drilled holes with the exact amount of spawn impregnated sawdust with minimal effort. The holes are then sealed with hot food wax to keep the spawn moist. The logs are then ready to stack in a shady part of the woods while the fungi begin to colonise. This takes between one to two years depending on the type of wood used. For example, birch will be colonised much quicker than oak or sweet chestnut. If left in a stack they will start to produce mushrooms the autumn after colonisation is complete. In order to reap an earlier and/or more regular crops, the logs can be shocked into fruiting by immersing them in water. This stimulates a change in climatic conditions and the mycelium responds in pure survival mode by producing more mushrooms. Logs can be shocked three to four times a year. Shocking involves forty eight hours in water (I throw them in the pond) and then mushrooms appear five to seven days later. So by rotating the logs, and timing how many are shocked, it is possible to be fairly accurate if you want mushrooms for a particular meal or to supply a certain

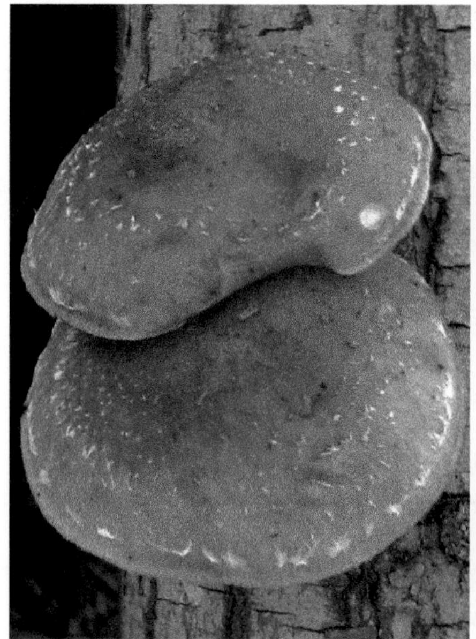

gastro-pub in time for the bank holiday weekend. Mushroom logs provide a high value return to the woodsman. The timber used would otherwise be firewood. Both the inoculated logs and mushrooms by the kilo can be sold and it is always good to know that what looks like a pile of rotting logs to the untrained eye is in fact a log larder to the woodsman.

With the standards down, we spend a few more days making pales for chestnut paling fencing before taking down the shelter that has been our base for the coppicing season. It has sheltered us through winter and seen the seasons pass from leaf fall through to the buds beginning to burst. I break out the first gallon of Prickly Nut Wood cider, made the previous October. With the first apple trees beginning to blossom this is time for celebration, a time to reflect on the hard work of winter and for the apprentices a moment to feel proud, their first coppicing season completed. I can only hope the desire and need to return to this ancient cyclical practice is now embedded within them and three more woodsmen will be cutting next winter. For me it is the end of yet another coppicing season. It is the most satisfying of winter work. I am proud to be part of this ancient tradition, far removed from the huge timber harvesters of the 21st century. These woodlands are part of our heritage, a wonderful renewable resource. Worked and shaped by woodsmen for generations to supply a sustained yield of timber, their time has come again to be valued, worked and appreciated.

***Far left: Mushroom inoculation.***

***Left middle: Detail of inoculation.***

***Near left: Shiitake mushrooms fruiting at Prickly Nut Wood.***

***Above: As the pales pile up, winter work draws to a close.***

As March draws to a close, and with the coppicing season behind me, spring is beginning to burst and I am moving with the transition. Walking across the common, the starry flowers of the blackthorn (*Prunus spinosa*) shine back at me awaiting pollination to form the sloes that will become the gin I will enjoy during the depths of next winter. The goat willow (*Salix caprea*) is the first real nectar flow for the bees and the sight and sound of their activity fills me with the promise of warmer weather ahead.

Food in the vegetable garden is

becoming scarce by late March. Most of the winter crops are coming to the end and the spring crops are not yet ready to eat. An unwelcome visitor has been attacking the perennial broccoli but one that will make a fine meal in return. The wood pigeon (*Columba palumbus*) can devastate agricultural crops or the woodsman's vegetable patch. Patience and stillness are required to shoot a wood pigeon with an air rifle. A head shot with the Weihrauch guarantees me one of my favourite meals. Laid on a bed of wild garlic with steamed nettles

***Left:* Goat or pussy willow.**

***Below left:* Intoxicating scent of wild garlic, one of woodland's finest salad vegetables.**

***Above:* Blackthorn in flower, often marks the last cold snap of winter.**

***Below:* The beautiful flowers of wild garlic.**

# Alder (*Alnus glutinosa*)

A native, light demanding pioneer species.

*Growing conditions:*
Tolerates very wet conditions, very hardy, naturally regenerates well, good species for reclaiming degraded land.

*Silvicultural practice:*
Deep rooted tree and therefore has good wind resistance and is often used in shelterbelts. Coppices well and is often used as a nurse crop. Fixes nitrogen by extracting it from the air through a relationship with a bacterial micro-organism of the genus 'Frankia' and then fixes it back into the soil through root nodules. Hence useful in mixed plantings to trees growing around it.

*Uses:*
Boardwood
Brush heads
Carvery
Charcoal
Clog soles
Dye from bark
Firewood
Furniture
Mushroom logs for shiitake
Nitrogen fixing
Pallets
Pulpwood
River protection
Tool handles
Toys
Turnery
Underwater foundations
Workshop floorboards

***Right: Colourful catkins of alder in march.***

***Left: The unmistakeable vibrant colour of freshly cut alder logs.***

## Pigeon Breast with Fruit Port Sauce

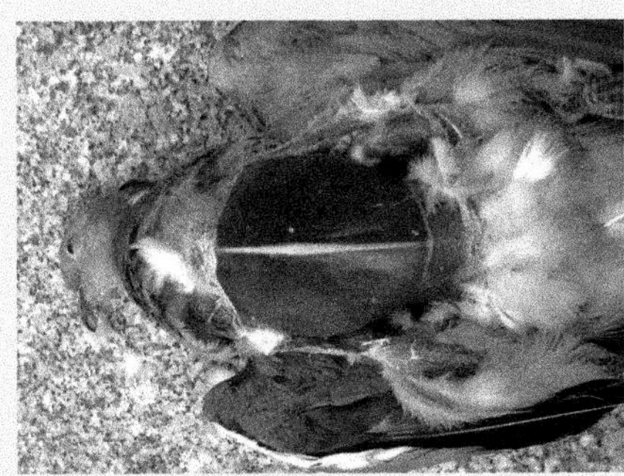

Although the whole pigeon can be used, the breast is where the majority of the meat lies and it is a quick and easy process to pluck a few breast feathers, cut and then peel back the skin to reveal the breast. Work round the breast bone with a small sharp knife to remove the breast meat. Young pigeons are very tender and preferable for this recipe.

Breast of two wood pigeons
1 onion
1 clove garlic
Olive oil

Choose a heavy frying pan and caramelise onions in olive oil. Add crushed clove of garlic and fry pigeon breasts over medium heat for three minutes each side. Place on a bed of wild garlic and serve with steamed nettles. (Steam nettles for longer than most green vegetables to remove presence of sting.)

*For the sauce:*
½ cup mixed fruit
1 cup port
1 oz butter
½ teaspoon cinnamon (ground)
3 whole cloves

Soak the mixed fruit in ½ pint hot water for 15 minutes, then drain. Mix the remaining ingredients in a pan and bring to the boil, reduce until thick and syrupy. Add seasoning and mixed fruit and simmer for ten minutes. Pour over pigeon breast just before serving.

# MARCH in Hampshire with Mark Howard

as accompaniment this is a delicious seasonal woodland dish.

Traditionally the cutting year would begin with leaf fall and the first frost in November, carrying on through the winter and ending on 31st March. There were seasonal variations to this of course. For many rural workers the end of harvest and any autumn cultivation work would coincide with work beginning in the woods. A few would work for themselves as woodland offered a first step towards self-employment and the start of a family business without the requirement of large amounts of land and capital. The majority were employed by coppice merchants on a piecework basis, paid by area cut or product produced. As the urban population grew in the 19th century and early 20th centuries so did the demand for coppice products, especially hazel. The activity in the woods was staggering: pea and bean sticks by the wagon load to the market gardens around London; fagots for domestic and industrial bakeries; crate rods to the potteries; and for the more skilled, thatching spars and sheep hurdles to be made, normally where the hazel was cut; and not forgetting stakes and binders for hedgelaying, to name but a few.

This seasonal work pattern is as true today as it was then. It is rare, to say the least, to find anyone that survives purely from coppicing or making hurdles although I do make to order throughout the year.

Remember long cold winters, or at least prolonged periods of frost? As I write this in the second week in January, there are primroses out, bluebells pushing through deep leaf litter and clumps of shiny green Lords and Ladies where I'm cutting.

Hazel was generally coppiced at between eight and 10 years of age for hurdlemaking. Now, with our warmer, wetter climate, I'm having to cut at five years old before the hazel gets too thick, consequently the growth rings are wider apart. This could have a marked effect on the longevity of the final product.

I have found from hard won experience that hazel cut in March will keep until mid to late June, and sometimes early July. I leave the cut hazel in heaps and work it up (trimming off any side shoots and cutting to length) only when required. The longer I can leave the rods untrimmed, the slower the drying process. Like most coppice crafts the wood is worked green. Cleaving fresh cut hazel is pure joy compared to splitting wood in July!

***Top: Mark Howard.***

***Left: The only way to remove hazel from the coppice.***

***Top right: Splitting hazel with a billhook.***

***Below right: Wood anemone.***

March also requires of me a continuous act of faith as I cut hazel: My order book may only contain a few weeks' work, but cut I must as without sufficient stocks of hazel I cannot take any orders – a very wooden Catch 22! This would be viewed as commercial madness by any businessman. Most of my products are for garden use and as spring takes its first few tentative steps my order book begins to fill. However, the demand for natural products, in particular hazel, has been affected by some good local and national government backed marketing in the early to mid nineties. Although this promoted sales of hurdles, unfortunately it also led to lorry loads of poor quality imported panels flooding the market that are often advertised for use in situations least suited, e.g. compost bins! The panels are easily recognised, they have no woven start and finishes, no turns to hold the panel tightly together, and are normally made using round rods. If the rods are halved then they've been through a circular saw and are then held together with nails. Just a small marketing challenge to add to my act of faith!

Each year as I stand and look at the coppice I need to cut, I'm slightly daunted by the task I've set myself. Physical work can have its benefits. As the hazel falls to my chainsaw and the coupe is gradually replaced with neat heaps of rods, their butts for the best part in line, and the white of the freshly cut stools stand out in stark contrast to the greening woodland floor, contentment takes hold for a while. The distinct smell of cut hazel and briar scent the air as I stand, perhaps too long, and listen to the chaffinch's spring call. I watch a comical wren, his body motionless, head turning from side to side as if driven by clockwork, whilst he sings his territorial song for all to hear.

It would be easy to be momentarily fooled by the ordered piles of rods, a misguided human need perhaps to create order out of nature. I work on. As a rough guide I normally allow approximately 10 days to cut an acre which, if the coppice is grade 1, should give me between 8-12,000 rods. There's no doubt I am happiest cutting hazel when it's of this quality; stools that are close together draw the rods up in a natural search for the light, and this stops them becoming over thick. The most productive way to make a hurdle is to split each rod once without having to cleave them down to a manageable size. Time, as always, is money. Grade 1 hazel coppice, however, is a very rare commodity and jealously guarded by hurdlemakers. The reality in most cases is a small area of grade 1 in a sea of grade 2, and at worse grade 3. Time and time again I've walked into a copse and been fooled by the good stools, only to find that I've had to thrash my way through poor quality hazel to get to the best, a case of not seeing the wood for the trees! Whatever size stand of hazel you buy it's an unwritten rule that everything must be cut, whether it is deer damaged, over stood, bramble enveloped, or species other than hazel. Providing I end up with at least 8-9,000 rods of hurdlemaking quality to get me through the main season I shall be content. I will occasionally use sallow and ash in my hurdles, following the old hurdlemaker's mantra: never waste anything that's been cut.

Experience has taught me that storing the hazel in heaps is a compromise between speed of working up – the less time moving between cut material – and the length of time the hazel will store. The bigger the heap, the less air is able to circulate, and this is an ideal environment for rot producing bacteria. This process can be accelerated if the woodland floor is carpeted in bluebells, and made even worse in combination with thunder. When labour was cheap and plentiful, this would have sent coppice workers scurrying back to the wood to stack rods vertically against any standard tree available to reduce potential damage.

So my hazel is cut, now all that is required are days of methodically working up. The standard trees, sometimes referred to as maidens, stand out against a hurrying March sky, wardens of the yet dormant underwood.

The delicate white heads of wood anemones track the course of the still low sun. Look closer and you will see that some may have a faint mauve blush. I prefer their colloquial name of 'windflower', as they can be battered by March winds. My guilt about stepping on this verdant carpet is tempered by knowing that the ancient practice of coppicing has created this soon-to-be bounty of colour: orchid, spurge, violet, stitchwort, archangel, ground ivy, anemone, dog's mercury, strawberry, primrose and our beloved bluebell, to name but a few, all benefit from the unrestricted sunlight warming the woodland floor.

As I work through the cut hazel orderly piles of marketable material grow around me, I need to work up initially sufficient hazel to meet a number of early, regular annual orders. These are between 10,000 and 12,000 pea sticks (used for herbaceous plant supports) the bulk of which are destined for London, and 1,000 bean rods next to growing numbers of round rods (used to start and finish a hurdle) and cleaving rods help me make steady inroads into my stock.

As dusk descends and the woodland edge softens against the darkening sky, our young Labrador reminds me of more pressing needs – a walk – then

***Bottom left: Primrose is a sign of oncoming spring in a broadleaf woodland.***

***Right: Opening the hazel fibres before turning the weaver around the end zale.***

***Below: The finished product ready to leave the woods.***

APRIL

# APRIL in Prickly Nut Wood

as we leave, a blackbird's alarm call sets off a cock pheasant, then another and another... then silence.

April is a magical month in Prickly Nut Wood – spring is bursting all around me. I am totally ready for spring, the hard winter of coppicing and squelching down muddy tracks has come to an end. The season has changed and with it so has my work. I won't fell another tree until November and I am now entering the creative phase of the woodland year. The lush greens of early spring, dappled sunshine and abundant wild flowers make the creative juices start to flow.

I return to an area of hazel, coppiced the previous year and I am impressed with the range of dormant wild flowers that have responded to the recoppicing and entrance of light. Violets, primroses, bluebells and early purple orchid – nature is a fine gardener. I can see the white blossom of a wild cherry grove in the copse beyond, a white beacon amongst the fresh new green growth.

The bluebells are abundant once more. It is easy to take for granted this vibrant hue of blue, but our bluebell woods are unique. You will not find them anywhere else on your travels. The flowering carpet of the bluebell in a broadleaf woodland is truly one of the wonders of the world. A colour therapist once told me that the shade of the bluebell against the brown of a tree stem and the lush green leaves of spring is one of the

***April title page:***
***Buds of sweet chestnut on the verge of 'springburst'.***

***From top left clockwise:***
***Primrose; Wild cherry in blossom; Early purple orchids with bluebells; Wild cherry blossom; Violets.***

***Facing page:***

***Left: Author peeling chestnut poles with a billhook.***

***Middle: Chickens, weeding and manuring part of the vegetable garden at Prickly Nut Wood.***

***Right: Freshly laid eggs.***

***Below: Steam bent one piece yurt hoop and other woodland produce at Prickly Nut Wood.***

calmest combinations of colour and time spent sitting in such an environment helps reduce symptoms of stress.

Living amongst them, it would be too easy to take these sights for granted, but we don't. Everyday I am thankful to be living the woodland way and a family bluebell picnic is an essential part of the woodland year. My own excitement about the beauty of the woods at this time is only surpassed when I see the expressions of joy and amazement from my children who have seen their winter walks amongst dark stems and mud transformed into this serenity of nature's blue.

We are currently constructing a yurt and components are being formed in and around the workshop. Yurts are a high added value product, the market for which has been increasing over the past ten years. Made from small diameter coppice poles, usually ash or sweet chestnut, yurts are in demand for temporary dwellings, teaching spaces, studios, play houses or luxury tents. Some yurt makers have moved into the hire market where weddings and themed parties create a demand. The original design is of Asian origin and it is a very strong and aesthetically pleasing design. Designed to cope with gale force winds and sub zero temperatures, these beautiful constructions make good homes for wood-land dwellers. There is constant activity in the making of them: peeling, drilling, sanding and tying together of trellis – but the highlight is the steam bending of the crown or hoop. I bend the hoops out of one piece of sweet chestnut about 4 inches diameter which is cleaved and worked with a draw knife before spending three hours in my custom made hoop steamer. Then, using a cast iron wheel form and bending pole, the wood is forced to shift its fibres and be transformed from a straight length into a round hoop. There is always satisfaction once this is achieved and with three apprentices experiencing such radical transformation of the nature of wood for the first time, discussion is soon flowing over the possibilities of different jigs to produce different shapes, typical of the creativity that the steam bending process can unlock.

The hens are laying well again and as I

## Spring Herb Omelette

3 freshly laid eggs
Splash of milk
Seasoning
1 onion
Handful of wild garlic leaves
Sprig wild marjoram
Thin slice of local hard cheese
Olive oil

Place a heavy frying pan on the fire and sauté onion in olive oil. Remove onions and add omelette mixture, well beaten eggs, milk and seasoning to pan. Allow omelette to firm slightly, then add onions, cheese, chopped wild garlic and chopped sprig of marjoram. Cover pan and cook over medium heat for a few minutes. Fold omelette in half and serve.

gather the last of the wild garlic and the fresh growth of wild marjoram, a favourite omelette graces the breakfast table.

April also heralds my first Open Day of the year. Since 'The Woodland House' gained notoriety thanks to Channel 4's Grand Designs programme, I have received a lot of requests from people wishing to visit the house and woods. In order to manage my time efficiently and respond to public interest, I have two or three ticketed open days a year. These are far more in depth than a tour of the house. In fact the house is the final part of a day where the management of the woods, types of product, uses in the building industry, craft uses, woodland food all set the context to why the house gained planning permission to be built in the first place.

***Top left: Explaining mushroom inoculation during Open Day circular walk.***

***Top right: Wood spurge.***

***Bottom left: Bugle.***

***Bottom right: Looking across part of last year's cut.***

The sun is shining and the late arrivals have been shepherded up to my outdoor kitchen where tea and conversation are flowing around the fire. I give a talk on the history of the woodland and how I ended up living and working at Prickly Nut Wood, before starting a circular walk through the woodland. All along the route, the questions keep coming and I stop in a number of places to explain the management and uses of the coppice. I cleave out a few poles and then we climb to the top of the hill and join the bridleway. From here we pass through some ancient wood pasture. Holly has colonised the wood pasture, as grazing animals (with the exception of deer) have not been present in the wood for some time. A pollarded beech on a woodbank marks a boundary long since forgotten.

Dropping back down into the chestnut coppice, we encounter the sadly familiar sight of *Rhododendron Ponticum*. When I first started working these woods, the rhododendron was rampant. Stems 6 inches thick with twisted branches reached up into the woodland canopy. Rhododendron coppices, seeds, suckers and layers and it is hard not to admire the colonising survival tactics of this plant. It can however form a dark, evergreen

***Right: Rhododendron entwined with chestnut coppice.***

## Pollarding

Pollard is the term used to describe a broadleaf tree that has been cut during the dormant season 6ft (1.8m) or more above the ground. The tree sends up shoots in a similar manner to a coppice stool but is cut at a height where animals cannot graze the re-growth of young shoots. The pollard poles are cut on a rotation and used in a similar way to coppice wood.

Pollards are often seen on woodbanks (boundary banks subdividing or surrounding a wood), along river banks (usually willow cut on a short rotation for thatching spars or basketry), in towns (often limes or London planes), or in parkland (often oak or beech). An ancient pollard on a woodbank has historical interest as well as being a useful habitat, but from a management point of view climbing pollards to cut timber is labour intensive and not the safest of occupations. Beech is recommended as a pollard as it doesn't coppice as well as other broadleaves.

***Left: Pollarded willow allows grazing by Jacobs sheep.***

***Right: Pollarded oak.***

covering across the woodland floor and above, ensuring that wild flowers and natural regeneration of tree species cannot occur. With the help of many people we have cleared 50 acres of rhododendron. Some has been totally eradicated. This has been by cutting and chipping all woody growth and then spot spraying the regrowth with a herbicide under agreement with Natural England. Other areas have begun to regrow and need cutting again and a large amount of seed has blown in from nearby gardens and surrounding woods to ensure that rhododendron control will remain part of my woodland year for many years to come.

Earlier this month, my neighbours who border the woodland, Michael and Julie Harrison, spent a lot of time cutting back rhododendron regrowth in order that it will be ready for spot spraying this summer. I am fortunate that there are some people living on the edge of the woodland who care about its health and long term wellbeing as I do.

My open day walk continues through this year's cut coppice, which is just beginning to reshoot, and then on through different aged cants, past charcoal kilns and mushroom log stacks, and then back to the woodland house for lunch. A book and tool stall has been set up on one of the verandas and there is a good deal of networking and exchanging of contacts before we begin the afternoon circuit of orchards, gardens, buildings and the woodland house itself. By late afternoon I grab a cup of tea and sit for a few moments on the old leather sofa by the fire. There is enough evening light now to play with the children in the garden before they go to bed. The see-saw I made them at Christmas is getting good use. As the light begins to fade and the woodcock circles overhead, I wander further into the wood where a charcoal kiln is ready to light.

The arrival of spring awakens the dormant gardeners from their slumber and they all want a hurdle, a rustic bench or a rose arch tomorrow. A lot of my products are targeted towards the garden market so it is of no surprise that this is a busy time.

In the modern world of business where people expect what they want to arrive at the press of a button, I find it refreshing to find people sympathetic to the fact that this produce is seasonal and although poles can be left in the shade or wrapped to try to keep moisture in to extend the season, it is best to order early and be prepared to wait a little time for many products. None of the woodsman I know are sitting in the wood, staring at their mobile phone hoping it will ring to help sell the vast stock of ready made hurdles stacked high in the coppice clearing. Most are making products to order as they come in and if this is not the case for you it is most likely that you are just starting out. Keep going, the orders will come – with a little marketing!

In addition to garden products, the warm weather is bringing out the barbecues and the increase in charcoal orders is keeping us busy. Because so much of the coppice was overstood, charcoal was one of the first products I made when I started at Prickly Nut Wood. It provided a good way of utilising a large volume of poor quality wood while I was getting the coppice back on cycle. I was also concerned to find that so much of our charcoal is imported, incurring large amounts of timber miles, and some could be sourced to sensitive areas such as rainforest and mangrove swamps. The need to buy local could not be clearer. As the years have passed and a lot of my coppice is back on cycle, some of the charcoal I now produce comes from the waste produced from other woodland products I am making. When constructing arbours, pergolas and erecting fencing a large number of

***Above: New shoots emerging from the coppiced chestnut stool.***

***Left: The book stall at Prickly Nut Wood Open Day.***

***Right: Charcoal kiln burning well.***

***Top right: Bagging up the last burn.***

***Bottom right: Oily considering her charcoal sales pitch.***

off-cuts accumulate. These can add up to a tonne or more of timber over the woodland year and that mixed with the rougher wood cut from the coppice forms the bulk of material which I convert to charcoal.

Charcoal burning stands out from the other woodland crafts and activities I am involved in because it involves night work. This means nocturnal outings into the heart of the woodland to move chimneys or make small adjustments to ensure a good and even burn, but it also gives me that privileged space of sitting quietly next to a warm glowing kiln when most of the northern hemisphere world is asleep. I enjoy being awake at a time when many humans are sleeping, for woodland life is awake and busy. Most mammals have worked out that it is safer to hunt and show their presence while humans sleep. Sitting by the kiln, listening in the darkness to the prolific sounds of rustling and scurrying and the occasional scream, the woods regain their wild edge and I become just another mammal, silently listening before following my track back to my home. Full moon charcoal burns bring this night time activity into vision, the rustling sounds form shapes, fox or badger if I am lucky, often just a wood mouse with so much noise and activity from one so small. My favourite visit to the kiln is the dawn check. A visit in April to a gently puffing kiln, as the first notes of the dawn chorus increase rapidly into an audible feast of birdsong, is one of those experiences that carves its way deep into the memory and leaves you with a satisfied smile, and you know whatever your day brings that smile will stay with you. Add to that a deep red sun rising through the waves of smoke hovering gently over the woodland floor and you can be forgiven for a momentary lapse in senses as you wonder whether you have become 'enlightened'. Of course all moments have their opposite and two days later

# Beech (*Fagus sylvatica*)

A native broadleaf species thought to be indigenous only to the southern Midlands, East Anglia and the south of England, but now widely naturalised across the British Isles.

*Growing conditions*:
Will grow in a wide range of soil types from acid through to alkaline. Favoured soil is slightly alkaline. Avoid frost pockets and poorly drained soils.

*Silvicultural practice*:
Traditionally pollarded and used in wood pasture where the nuts were enjoyed by grazing animals. Coppices poorly and is grown as a plantation tree often with a nurse crop. Useful species in continuous cover forestry as it is very tolerant of shade.

*Uses*:
Boardwood
Chair legs
Charcoal
Chopping blocks
Firewood
Flooring
Furniture
Interior joinery
Mushroom log host for tree oyster
Nut cases used in potpourri
Nuts produce edible oil and fodder
Plywood
Pulpwood
Spoons
Steam bending
Turnery
Veneer

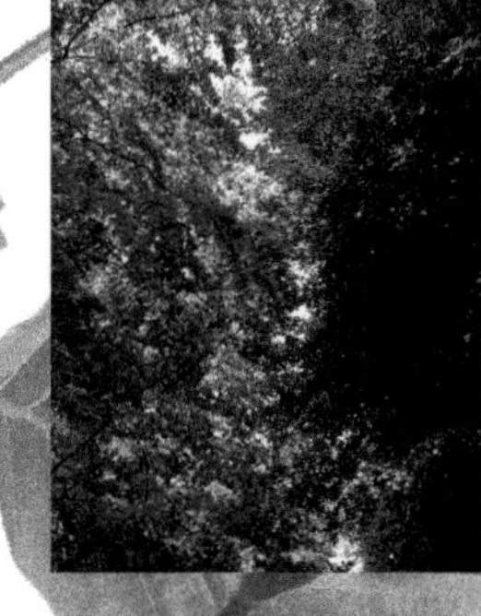

***Top left: Beech.***

***Top right: Beech canopy over ride.***

***Bottom: Beech nuts forming.***

## Beech Leaf Noyeau

This recipe has become well sought after amongst wild food tipple drinkers. For good reason, this is a liqueur I would choose in the highly unlikely event I was visited by travelling royalty or a passing poacher.

1 bottle gin
8oz (225g) sugar
1 large glass brandy
Beech leaves

Based on recipe from *Food for Free* by Richard Mabey.

Collect young, fresh, soft beech leaves and strip them from their stems. Place in jar and then pour over gin and leave for three weeks. Strain from the leaves. Boil sugar in half pint of water and add brandy and mix with gin. Bottle and enjoy. I particularly enjoy this liqueur warmed, it is a fine tonic on a cold winter's night in the woods.

# APRIL in the Ceiriog Valley with Stewart Whitehead

you will be sweating in overalls and a dust mask, emptying the kiln of its contents prior to reloading for the next burn.

I was born in 1961 in Warrington. Originally trained in fine art, I started working life as a sign writer on Anglesey (North Wales). Living on this holy isle taught me the values of self sufficiency from inshore fishing, gardening, land management and animal husbandry. Cutting firewood on a local country estate sparked my interest in the use of wood and kindled my affinity with trees.

I learnt chairmaking and pole turning from Tim Wade in 1990. Since that time I have continued to learn many more ancient and almost forgotten skills, some of which go back to the Bronze Age. I have worked alongside some of the past masters of woodland crafts in Britain and gained knowledge that has been passed down through both practical and oral tradition.

Keeping these old country ways alive and passing these crafts on to future generations is very important to me; I have mentored many wonderful people over the years. I call myself an artisan, preferring the term to 'craftsman' because of the association of contemporary crafts and the growth of non-functional crafts on display at craft fairs.

In 1997 I moved to the Ceiriog valley and started to work from Coed Brongyll, making my wares from our truly sustainable woodland.

As daylight intensity increases after the spring equinox, the woodland awakens. The plants on the woodland floor have taken advantage of the available light from early spring and the overwhelming smell of wild garlic (ransoms) carries on the wind. We use the garlic as flavouring, the leaves in salads with dandelion, hawthorn leaves, and wood sorrel. Young nettles grow at an alarming rate in the nitrogen rich soil; these make for a good tonic in soups flavoured with wild thyme. Another favourite is nettle beer, only taking a week or so to make. Wild strawberries mixed with primroses line the track ways with their dainty flower heads standing to attention. Dog's mercury and yellow archangel come into flower and ferns unroll their new throngs throughout the woodland. Trees start flowering, being pollinated by bees, insects and the wind. Cherry blossom shines out in the woodland canopy of the Ceiriog valley.

The hawthorn (whitethorn) is in full leaf with white blossom forming almost a halo around it. It was once called bread and cheese as the leaves and flowers are edible. The whitethorn is the tree of

***Top:***
***Stewart Whitehead.***

***Left:***
***Cottage and yurt in woods.***

April in our ancient Celtic Ogham lunar calendar; it symbolizes fertility, cleansing, protection and the coming of summer; at Beltaine (May Day) it is one of the first trees to come to life. The Ogham is an alphabet and language that relates to trees and their spirits, our ancients believed them to be gateways to deeper wisdoms.

Coed Brongyll is situated on the north east borderlands of Wales. I live in the middle of this broadleaf woodland, in the beautiful winding Ceiriog Valley, the naming of the valley relating in Welsh to 'wild cherry'.

The woodland was mainly oak, ash, and cherry with hazel understorey, on a very steep south east facing side of the valley. Because of virtual clear felling in World War II, a rich mix of sycamore, birch, willow, rowan, whitethorn, elm, holly and elder have crept in, most of the oaks were removed. The oaks relate back to one of the oldest oaks in Britain which stands behind our local village Pontfadog.

When we came here, there had been no management of the woodland for nearly 60 years. Over the years of living here I have coppiced derelict hazels that were dying and falling over, creating soil erosion on the steep slopes. Thinning out the canopy and leaving the straightest trees for the future gives the woodland floor more light, so increasing the biodiversity. I created paths using brash to reinforce the outer edges of the pathways so enabling me to extract timber using my native fell pony, Tom.

Each time I recoppice I layer hazel to increase the stool density. Replanting is not necessary as nature does it for itself, but a little human interaction can place seedlings into empty spots in the wood. In 1998, I received a merit award from the Forestry Commission for managing Coed Brongyll in a traditional and sustainable way.

April is the time of the year I take stock of the materials that have been harvested over the winter months; nearly all the coppicing and felling is done and the woodland copses are left alone, unless there is oak or elm for peeling. Each winter I coppice and thin approximately 1 acre (more like 1½ acres being on a steep slope) of our own woodland, dressing out and grading the sticks into bundles of produce as I work through the winter months.

Hazel is made up into hurdles on the rain free days in spring and rakes, rustic furniture and yurts are made over the summer. Small diameter timber for turning is stacked near the workshop to be worked up through the coming months. I'm always looking to increase the value and diversity of my crop and any larger timber is converted into planks on a Norwood mobile band saw owned by our local woodworkers' co-operative. Firewood is an important crop as it is one of our main sources of energy and splitting and stacking is an important job in the spring, so it can dry out over summer. I also produce a small amount of charcoal for barbecues and forging tools.

On the warm days in April tree buds start to burst open, the rising tree sap can be tapped and utilised in many ways. Tapping into the rising sap of the birch and sycamore for wine making is very rewarding come the cold winter solstice!

As spring is getting warmer, bark peeling can start as early as the middle of April. I learnt to peel tan bark from Bill Hogarth who was the last coppice

***Above:***
***Wild garlic pathway.***

***Middle:***
***Wood sorrel.***

***Right:***
***May blossom.***

merchant in Cumbria. What a wonderful man he was, full of stories from a time when the woods were full of woodsmen and women.

If sap is rising in a tree it can be felled and the bark can be peeled straight away. To see if the sap is flowing well I use a use a billhook, brazing just under the bark to check if the bark releases easily from the wood. With oak I usually fell four stems with a chainsaw, cut to length and raise up to waist height on two big forked sticks driven into the ground and then peel them with a special barking iron. It is necessary to only cut a small quantity of wood at a time as the weather in April can be very changeable and all felling ceases if it gets cold.

The peeled poles are self-extracting if you work on a slope as they are extremely slippery when first peeled. The bark is stacked under a big tree and left to dry out over the summer before it is collected by the tannery. You can get a good price per ton for bark, but it takes a lot of peeling. The sound of peeling bark has a beauty to it, clicking away as you part the bark from the wood. I like peeling the forked branches for furniture; stacked up against a standard tree they take on a sculptural form. Bark peeling can go on into July.

Oak bark is very rich in tannin in the spring and is valuable for tanning leather, or should I say was, as there is only one oak bark tannery left in Britain, J & FJ Barkers & Co in Devon. It's a terrible shame, as the management of oak woodland was once a huge rural employer.

The tanning of leather for boot makers and saddlers was essential in rural life before oil. I have a leather working harness for my fell pony which is bark tanned – it's about 150 years old and is still in good working order. In Wales most towns and some villages had a tannery; whole families would go into the woods to cut and peel oak, but not anymore. I believe this will turn around as oil related industries burn out and we revert back to more traditional ways for a greener future.

All materials come finally to my workshop. Standing perched on a hillside terrace just down from the cottage, a wooden ramp leads off a track into a covered timber building on stilts. Upstairs there's an area for bench work, like chair and yurt wheel assembly; below I convert timber into produce by cleaving, axing and shaving.

From smaller diameter straight timber I turn parts for Windsor and Welsh stick chairs on a pole lathe, also turning domestic treen ('treen' meaning 'of a

***Above:***
***Hazel coppice at Coed Brongyll.***

***Below left:***
***Workshop, yurt and hurdles.***

***Below right:***
***Side axing a billet.***

tree', therefore any product made of wood). I love making things that have an everyday function in the home, bowls, spoons and rolling pins, to name a few.

Carving a Welsh cawl spoon from sycamore or cherry is time consuming but infinitely rewarding. Cherry, ash, sycamore and oak all make beautiful furniture, but my favourite is yew, which I prune with reverence from local ancient trees. Timber for steam bending tends to be sawn but cleft wood is also used for chairs. Ash is perfect for yurts, utilising its qualities to bend and withstand shock.

The woodland has a wide variety of birds, animals and insects. The spring is the time of nest making, mating and raising young. I always leave fruiting trees like rowan, whitethorn, holly and elder in the wood to feed the wildlife later on in the year. A large rookery occupies the very top part of the wood. As night falls the noisy flock settles into their nesting site and the bats, owls and badgers emerge into the night to start hunting. In the daytime woodpeckers tap away at trees, and blackbirds, wrens, robins and blue tits sing their hearts out. A small flock of long tail tits flit into a tree, spread throughout its branches hunting for food, then just as quickly off they dart.

There are many buzzards which patrol the woodland canopy, looking for mice, voles and shrews on the woodland floor. They gather, circling high above the valley on warm rising thermals.

April is full of vibrant energy; you can really feel the woodland spirits twinkling away in the undergrowth... or maybe it was just an elusive dormouse waking up after its winter hibernation.

And as the month finally draws to its close, the sight and scent of the bluebells and Welsh poppies mark the closing of the woodland canopy. The trees

***Below:***
***Chairs and other wares.***

MAY

unfold their new and luminous emerald leaves for further growth in the fast approaching summer.

The woodlands are lush in anticipation of summer heat. Green shoots are sprouting and a wealth of edible leaves and plants have sprouted for the woodland forager. Temperatures sometimes rise to mid summer heat but the nights can be deceptively cool. Charcoal burning is picking up pace and timber framing projects are underway.

I am always amazed to see builders working on houses in the middle of winter, battling against the elements and the lack of light. In our climate, nature dictates that a building project should be underway by the beginning of May and be weather tight by the end of October. It is a pattern I have followed with all the constructions I have been involved with.

Timber framed buildings are part of our heritage, an evolving pattern over hundreds of years. These days most buildings are constructed from green oak, in the past many different timbers were used – poorer land based workers often making do with a mixture of different timbers, using what was locally available to them, while the wealthier land owners had the best of the oak for their houses.

As much as I admire the craftsmanship in many of the green oak timber frames I see constructed, most are now pre-fabricated in large workshops on

concrete floors, a world away from the woodlands they came from. For me the joy of building is in the whole process, from living tree to finished frame.

I built a green oak forestry barn with three other framers (*see photo series down right hand column*) and we individually chose each tree, felled them and extracted them with horses to the construction site (still within the woodland). We then milled the timber, built the frames and raised it. The trees turned into a barn without leaving the wood they were felled in.

Most of us do not have woods full of oaks waiting to be become timber frame buildings. But we may live in an area where there is chestnut coppice, like I used for the frame of the woodland house, or possibly softwood thinnings like the larch that we have extracted to construct my new workshop. I am now working primarily with timber framing using

***May title page: Rafters and battens attached.***

***Opposite page: Greening up.***

***Right, top to bottom:***
***1. Horses pulling sawmill to the construction site.***
***2. Oak being extracted and transported to the construction site.***
***3. Conversion of timber into beams.***
***4. The barn frame.***
***5. Barn prior to cladding.***

***Below: Scribing the profile of one chestnut log onto another, one of the many techniques used in roundwood timber framing.***

***Bottom: Roundwood barn at Pestalozzi International Village, built by the author and a team of trainee carpenters.***

roundwood. This is a construction method that uses durable small diameter roundwood poles and takes some of the techniques from traditional timber framing, and some of the scribing ideas from log cabin design, to create a new vernacular of low cost ecological building. This method is cheaper and the materials more readily available to people wanting to construct a house or barn on their land.

My workshop is to be a roundwood cruck frame construction, using a larch frame and will be built on pad foundations using no concrete, just pits of compacted stone or rubble.

I have been running a course for the frame construction and after four days the larch thinnings are now jointed and laid out ready for raising. A raising day is always full of anticipation, it is the high point of any build. For me it is a day of extreme focus, ensuring the safety of all personnel and giving clear instructions during the process. Today is no different, the frames lie stacked upon one another ready to be raised with a hand winch. Posts are being driven into the ground to tie off the ropes as the frames are raised. Everyone involved has a clear role. Knots are being tied, lines stretched out to the front and back of each frame. Prior to commencement, I take a walk to focus my mind and prepare for the intensity of the day.

The last of the bluebells can still be seen but the vibrance of the blue has gone. Yellow archangel (*Lamiastrum*

***Top left: Yellow archangel.***

***Above: Yellow pimpernel.***

***Below, left to right:***
***1. Workshop frame raising.***
***2. The cruck frames raised and braced.***
***3. Ropes and harness are used to fix the roof rafters.***

***Top right: Prickly Nut Wood pond – dipping pool, dragonfly haven and source of clay plaster.***

galeobdolon) and yellow pimpernel (*Lysimachia nemorum*) are freshening up the woodland floor. The leaf colour is pale and fresh and the occasional shower is keeping the rides from becoming dusty. I swing my arms and breathe deeply. The may (hawthorn) blossom casts a sweet yet musty scent, but the sound of a post being rammed into the ground focuses me back to the raising and I return refreshed from my stroll.

After a safety briefing the raising begins. The first part of the raise is always the most awkward with the winch determined to drag rather than lift the frames. Once the feet are stabilised on the pads, the frame gradually makes its way to its vertical position. Frame by frame the tree trunks stand up and form the skeleton of a building. By the end of the day the frames are all raised. It has been a successful five days.

A group of us take an evening stroll to celebrate with a beer and on our return are greeted by a long drawn 'pew pew pew' rising to a crescendo. We sit quietly beneath an oak and listen to the nightingale's song. It is the night time magic that highlights the beauty of this song. Such variety and climbing notes from such a small bird, when all else is silence, amplifies the shrill tones. An hour must have past us by and it is only the coolness of the night that encourages us to finish our journey and return to our beds.

With the crucks raised, a group of us work on with the jointing and pegging of jowl posts and tie beams and it is not long before we are fixing roof rafters. There is a timeless beauty in the gradual process of chiselling out joints and turning trees into a building. The weather has stayed dry and a dip in the woodland pond to cool off has become a regular activity at the end of the day. The pond was an old catchment pond for the brickworks many years ago. When I moved into the woods it was a

silted up rubbish dump, full of old milk crates and bottles and the edges had been encroached by the colonising goat willow (*Salix caprea*). I dug out the pond

*Above: Hazel arbour.*

and repuddled the clay and since then it has become an oasis for wildlife within the coppice, boasting an abundance of dragon and damsel flies, newts and numerous waterborne beetles and insects. There is one deep plunge pool where we sometimes take a dip, the water is always very cold as it is fed from the spring. Having acclimatised to the temperature, with my eyes at water level I once watched a grass snake zig-zagging across the water inches in front of me. The water temperature always ensures a quick dip but a nearby swinging bench provides an ideal spot to reflect on the watery surroundings.

An order for a small hazel arbour deters me from framing. To survive as a woodsman you have to be content to switch from one project to another as demand dictates. I have wrapped the hazel in tarpaulin to keep it moist and I am pleased to find it still supple. The arbour frame is a chestnut arch with steam bent poles to create a curved back. The weave gets tight near the top of the arch and I substitute some willow rods to allow more flexibility. Lunchtime beckons and I collect a woodland salad. It is a mixture of wild and self-sown greens with lime leaves forming the bulk. The elderflowers are ready for picking and a basket quickly filled with florets gives me enough for wine and a few fritters for lunch.

The last week of May and the roof rafters are fixed, but another break in the flow of framing is due as the village fete approaches. When you believe like I do in the importance of 'keeping it local', a stall at the village fete is always part of the woodland year. What I have available for a stall depends on how the winter has gone, how much I coppiced and what I have had time to make. Some years I have taken furniture, hurdles, walking sticks and charcoal but this year will be a more modest display. A van load of barbecue charcoal, some artists' charcoal and a couple of chestnut chairs with bark seats.

Most English villages have an annual fete to raise funds for community projects and almost everyone gets involved. I used to take a large chestnut pole and a couple of small 'A' frames and set up a greasy pole, where children had the pleasure of trying to knock one another off the washing-up liquid greased pole with pillows. Adults of course also had a go and children particularly enjoyed knocking their parents off the pole. It was always well attended but sadly even with mattresses beneath it, it has been banned as the fete insurers won't cover it. It will however reappear at my children's birthday parties.

The weather is good and I enjoy a local beer and an exchange of news with

## A May Woodland Salad

Lime leaves
Hawthorn leaves
Hazel leaves
Garlic mustard (Jack-by-the-hedge)
Wood sorrel
Chickweed
Wild marjoram
Chives
Raspberry leaves
Rocket

**Above: Lime leaf.**
**Right: Garlic mustard (Jack-by-the-hedge).**

old friends. The afternoon is busy and the prospect of a warm evening tempts some of the public into buying barbecue charcoal before they leave. I used to do a number of fetes, craft and wood fairs; but now with a busy order book, I am usually making products to demand rather than making and trying to sell. I pack up the stall and head home. The children are tired after the excitement of the day and by 7.30pm I am lighting the barbecue and Bev and I are able to absorb the tranquillity of the woodland evening. Sitting on the veranda with a glass of wine as the light starts to fade I reflect upon the fete and village life. So much has changed in the past twenty years. Many of the farms are no longer farming, relying on renting barns and buildings for industrial use and many barns have become houses, and only a handful of people are working the land. All around a touch of suburbia is encroaching upon the rural Sussex countryside, I guess inevitable on a small island with an increasing population. Then I hear a familiar sound, a 'churring' ringing out across the copse. The nightjar has returned, having escaped the dangers of a journey from Africa to return once again to these woods. It is the male who arrives first, marking his territory and calling for a female. He chooses the standard trees over the freshly cut coppice to let out his 'churring' call and then swoops with a clap of his wings to the next standard before he calls again. They will lay eggs on the ground. There is no nest, just a scratching to mark the spot where this camouflaged bird will lay. They will stay the summer and if it is a hot one, perhaps hatch a second brood before taking flight to the warmth of Africa.

The nightjar's song is reassuringly familiar. It touches a chord within me as it does every year and I am thankful

## Elderflower Wine

I have tried many recipes for elderflower wine and finally settled on this one. I don't make very much as I am always keen to see the flowers become berries and then there is a red and white wine off the same tree.

I pint elderflowers
2½lb sugar
½lb chopped raisins
2 lemons
I gallon water
White wine yeast

Pick flowers when fully open and cut from stems with scissors. Boil the water and pour over the flower petals. Add chopped raisins, sugar and juice of lemons. When cooled to body temperature add yeast, cover and leave to ferment for a week before staining into demijohn, fitting airlock and leaving to ferment. Rack it (siphon off from sediment) into another demijohn once it clears. It should be ready to bottle in about three months. Drink young.

## Elderflower Fritters

Make a pancake batter of:
4oz plain flour
½ cup of milk
½ cup of water
I egg

Beat thoroughly and then dip elderflower florets into batter by the stalk, and fry in hot oil. Cut stalk off and turn. Dust with sugar if required.

# Oak, Pedunculate / English (*Quercus robur*)
# Oak, Sessile (*Quercus petraea*)

The two native oaks of the British Isles. The two species are rarely separated as uses and timber quality are the same.

*Growing conditions*:
Tolerates most soils but needs soil depth for root growth. Avoid frost hollows. Avoid calcerous and very sandy soils as shake may occur. *Quercus robur* preferred on heavy clay soils.

*Silvicultural practice*:
Most dominant broadleaf timber species in Britain. Grown as high forest, climax species, standard over coppice, coppices freely, often now grown as a plantation.

*Uses*:
Bark used for tannin
Barrels
Buildings
Charcoal
Fencing
Fibre board
Firewood
Floor boards
Flour from acorn
Furniture
Gates
Hardwood pulp
Particle board
Rustic furniture
Shingles
Supports high number of invertebrates
Swill baskets
Timber framing
Trugs
Veneer
Wine from leaves

***Top: Clean stem, ideal for milling.***

***Top left: Queen Elizabeth Oak, a veteran tree in Cowdray Park, Sussex.***

***Above right: Oak window seat, floor and door.***

***Above left: Rays of oak, a popular feature sought by furniture makers.***

***Below right: Traditional oak swill basket.***

# MAY in Yorkshire with Geoff Norton & Angela Cole

it has returned. It is one of the signs I judge my woodsmanship by.

After months of enjoying the routine shared by most people, May brings the show season and almost every summer weekend is booked up before winter arrives. We used to travel as far north as Newcastle and as far south as Sheffield, but our range now stretches from Scotland to Gloucestershire. Craft demonstration pays at least twice as well as 'real' work, so its hard not to answer the call.

The calls come while we're still coppicing and thinning. We work in a few different woods: cutting hazel here, oak there, and a mixture of species in another. We cut until mid March and then switch focus completely for the rest of spring and summer. By May, a beautiful month in the woods with nature at full throttle, we've usually had weeks of making hazel hurdles and cleft oak fencing in the yard. Garden activity is in full swing and we make sales of rustic materials for climbing plants, edging paths and building structures. Hopefully we've also done a burn.

Charcoal is one of the products we like to show off at events and though it is bulky and a lot to carry for not much profit, it looks good stacked up in crisp brown sacks. It features one up from the bottom on a list of products ranging from firewood to timber framed structures. We use the kiln like a bin for anything that can't be made into a stake or a rail or a post. By adding as much value as possible to materials, we can just about make woodland work viable.

Angela demonstrates either pole lathe turning or willow work. I do hurdlemaking, something related to timber framing, or general green woodworking skills. We both found it challenging to work under the public eye at first, feeling like untrained charlatans a sliver away from public humiliation. In time you realise that most people are just happy to see traditional craft skills which many assume are dying arts. Common enquiries relate to the condition of your hands and the sharpness of your edge tools. Some people will stand and watch for a long time. Maybe even as long as an hour. If you start to speak, spectators edge forward and others stop and join the crowd.

Our show set up has grown with the addition of an apprentice, Ben Kelleher, sponsored by The Green Wood Centre/ Small Woods Association. Quiet, calm and capable, Ben already demonstrates spoon and bowl carving and is gaining other skills very quickly. He seems ready to travel anywhere at anytime and was only slightly ruffled by the ordeal of spending four days up front in the forestry arena at The Great Yorkshire Show.

Burning charcoal is a good thing to do in the three clear days between unloading from one show and loading for another. It's good to get a break from the crowds and, apart from cutting billets to length with a chainsaw, the filling of the kiln, the lighting, the emptying, grading and bagging can make for peaceful work in the woods. On the downside, it can be murder because using a chainsaw safely in summer means heavy clothes, a lot of sweat, and flies. Emptying the kiln could be done naked, and maybe even should be done naked as there's still a lot of sweat. Flies are less of a problem now, though, because of the dust. The dust is light, fine, and voluminous and if, like me, you've decided not to compromise your lungs so much these days you have to

***Top: Geoff and Angela with family.***

***Left: Oak framed gate with hazel infill.***

wear a mask. The mask is hot and sweaty. I tell myself I should do this job in winter, which would be lovely.

The weather is of course a national obsession and if you work outside a lot of the time it's practically a religion. We all know about May and shedding a clout and all that, but by this time of year we really are ready for things to start warming up. The show season, running from May-September, is payback time for winter and though we do get short changed now and then, generally it is good. Occasionally it rains buckets and one of us struggles to entertain bored kids just wanting to be at home. Sometimes we find ourselves being paid to work in the sun, our craftsmanship admired by a knowing public, our children playing happily in the shade. Sometimes, when the show fields are emptying, a trader takes a bag of charcoal and returns in the morning just to tell us how good it is!

The best part of charcoal making for me is when all four chimneys are warm enough to pull billowing plumes of white smoke up through the trees. That and driving steadily home along winding lanes with huge sacks filling the truck and a face like a miner. Skin has to be scrubbed clean in the shower and the eye-liner effect lasts for two days, by which time we hope to be selling the odd bag at the next show.

Shows are a source of income in themselves and a means of publicity. Organisers of other events rightly assume we can demonstrate for them, and demonstrations can bring us workshops and training jobs. Angela has taken a forest school qualification which has added another dimension to the educational services we can offer. The portfolio on the rustic bench has pictures of everything from the plant dibber the public can watch being turned, and maybe buy, right through to a community arts project.

The practicalities involved in the show season can take the edge off the fun of the travel and camping. We appreciate why haulage companies are attached to the word 'logistics' as we load our old pick-up to the gunnels and hitch our even older caravan. Vehicles are important to us. We dream of a Land Rover than can seat us all comfortably and carry a full show set-up, and pull a lovely vintage van with working electrics getting 25 miles to the gallon. Ours does 18 and burns oil.

We also have to think about school times, not exhausting the kids, gas bottles, setting up times, paperwork, shopping, buying a new bow-saw blade, not buying diesel on the motorway unless necessary and so on. We usually get back grubby and hungry late on Sunday night and carry sleeping children

***Above: A fedge of willow and hazel with mixed planting.***

***Right: Green oak cart shed arbour.***

***Opposite top: Tree spiral in hazel.***

***Opposite middle: Globe of willow and felt.***

***Opposite bottom: Green oak footbridge.***

to bed before lighting the fire and the stove and then, finally, opening a bottle of wine.

The following Monday morning in May is when people call and ask if you've got 20 x 6 feet hurdles they can collect tomorrow. This is not surprising if you call yourselves Yorkshire Hurdles and spend weekends demonstrating this craft and others behind a small stack of business cards. Unfortunately it doesn't work like that for us as everything apart from the firewood and charcoal is made to order from wood cut at the appropriate time of year, which is usually winter.

We try to make a weekend out of Monday and Tuesday between shows. This is very difficult when most people are working and the phone is ringing, and Tuesday can never feel like Sunday. We miss parties and barbecues and all sorts of activities with friends and family in summer and, worst of all, we're working when everyone's having fun. On the positive side, we tend to meet traffic jams coming the other way and the beach is quiet midweek. Come Wednesday, we have to think what materials we'll need for the next job.

We don't make much charcoal compared to some burners. It's hard to make it work business-wise without machinery and regular wholesale orders. We prefer to keep it simple and sell direct. As the show season rolls on we look to get on with commissions. If we can possibly plan for it, summer is the time for big jobs. Recent big jobs have included a green oak footbridge and a traditional truss for the roof in a watermill. Our workshop is small, so timber framing has to be done outside... slowly... with great attention to detail... using hand tools. Warm weather is very much preferred.

The experience of dealing with the public all day after the relative isolation of our lives in winter is at first a novelty and then a professional challenge. At major events, simply being surrounded by so many people for so long is draining. Also, it's not easy to give fresh sounding answers to the questions we are asked countless times. Jokes and banter make the days pass more easily but as the summer goes on we have to grit our teeth and try harder. In fact, considering the travelling time, the loading, the unloading, and the rest of it, craft demonstration isn't that well paid after all!

Then suddenly it's all over and the charcoal is gone. We feel relieved and satisfied and there's enough money in the bank not to worry about that for a little while. We can, hopefully, look at jobs that have come in and we can service our saws ready for the cutting season. We are looking forwards to

JUNE

# JUNE in Prickly Nut Wood

getting back into the woods, to cooler weather, to weekends. Six months later, we're looking forward to the shows. Early June and the area of coppice we cut last winter already looks totally different. The stools have now disappeared beneath a mound of fresh green stems and leaves, and the gaps between the stools are growing smaller. Over the next two months, the coppice stools will put on up to 2 metres of new growth. This is the most vigorous period of growth throughout the woodland year, you can almost watch it growing.

The dominant flower colour at this time is the purple haze of the foxglove (*Digitalis purpurea*), a biennial plant, it germinates the first year after the coppice has been cut and then the flowers appear in abundance the following summer.

I take a walk down the main ride to the larch plantation as I need to extract a few trunks I felled during the winter to mill up for floor joists for the workshop. The ride is edged with the flowers of red campion (*Silene dioica*) and the tall stems of the free seeding figwort (*Scrophularia nodosa*). The ride is showing signs of wear from the winter's work. The summer maintenance of rides is a good investment of time and ensures the surface is in sound condition for the following winter. Most years there is some work to be done, a trailer load or two of sandstone chippings or the building up of an eroding edge near a ditch with posts and boards. Rodding of pipes to ensure the water flows under rather than over the ride will help to keep the track in good condition for many years. It is often a challenge to allocate time for these more mundane activities but they are an important part

***June title page: Prickly Nut Wood oak cloaked in summer mantle.***

***Facing page: The astonishing regrowth of coppiced chestnut.***

***Top left: Hedge woundwort.***

***Top right: Figwort.***

***Bottom left: A flush of foxgloves follow me as I cut the coppice.***

***Below: Red campion.***

# PAWS

PAWS is the Forestry acronym for Plantations on Ancient Woodland Sites. There are many of these throughout the country and I have one area which I manage adjacent to Prickly Nut Wood. They were the forestry fashion of the 1950s and '60s and supported by the Forestry Commission. Many ancient woodlands were planted with conifer species for purely economic reasons. Forestry economics need to be viewed in cycles beyond the length of a human's lifetime. The short sighted economic hope was of a fast return in 40 years. In most cases it can now be seen that the economic forecasts were short sighted and the damage to the woodland flora and fauna underestimated. In some woodlands the broadleaf trees were felled and where regrowth occurred, it was sprayed with a chemical herbicide. Oliver Rackham makes reference to the tenacity of small-leaved lime in ancient woodland in Essex, which survived heavy doses of 2,4,S-T, one of the many chemicals used to defoliate prior to 'coniferisation'. How well the ancient woodlands have fared depends largely upon the species planted, ground preparation, management and of course climatic conditions. Trees that cast a heavy shade like western hemlock or Douglas fir will deplete all the ground flora below them over time; if the wind has caused some felling and allowed light through the canopy, however, both ground flora and native species will have had a chance to hang on. In woodland where heavy shade bearers seem to have destroyed the entire ground flora, dormant seed may still be waiting to return once light returns to the soil after felling. In more fortunate plantings, European larch was used. Larch is a deciduous conifer and one of the few species that has less of an impact on

the ground flora, but it still has the effect of acidifying the soil over time. Many PAWS are still standing, often as small blocks within ancient woodland which is expensive to remove – partly because of poor management, the timber has little economic value and the cost of felling and extraction often far outweighs the value of the timber itself. I felled a PAWS in a local wood in 1991. This was larch and it would have been uneconomic to fell and extract the timber; however by using a mobile sawmill, I converted the wood into useful timber for cladding and shed construction. It is a lot easier and less damaging to the woodland to take out planks rather than whole trunks.

So, what to do if you have a PAWS? First, carry out a full assessment of the woodland and consider what uses there are for the species planted. European larch and western red cedar are both species which produce very durable timber that can be used without chemical treatment for outside construction (houses, sheds, barns, stables, fencing etc.) So with these species mobile milling for home use may be the best option. Douglas fir produces a very stable building timber and is ideal for floor joists or roof rafters. With most other species, unless they have been well managed and the access into the woodland is good, it is likely to be fairly costly to remove the plantation. Forestry Commission grants are available for PAWS and this could help towards the cost of extraction or mobile milling. The price for softwood pulp would hardly pay to load the lorry let alone fell the timber; so if it is of poor quality, it is probably a better option to saw it up, season it and put it in the wood burner! Another option may be to move towards a continuous cover system removing some of the plantation and allowing natural regeneration to occur to create a mixed age forest.

An important last bit of advice. What do you do when the plantation is felled? The temptation is to plant up with native broadleaves; my advice in a PAWS situation is to wait and observe. The likelihood is that over time the woodland will regenerate with native species and a more natural and local seed based woodland will evolve. Remember, we are only here for a short time; our lifespan is but a rustle of a leaf in the life of the forest.

***Far left:***
***Plantation of hemlock and western red cedar has shaded out the ground flora of this ancient woodland.***

***Near left:***
***Larch, a deciduous conifer is less damaging to ground flora than evergreen conifers.***

***Below left:***
***Larch, a suitable species for roundwood timber framing.***

***Below right:***
***6 x 2 inch Douglas fir used for floor joists on a roundwood chestnut frame.***

of the management of the woodland, and I am always thankful the following winter that I have made the effort.

The dappled shade along the ride gives a pleasant balance contrasting the heat of the sun with the cool shady climate of the leafy woodland. I notice the swelling nuts on the tall stems of the beech overhanging the ride and then my eyes are taken higher still, attracted by the 'kiew' call of the buzzard (*Buteo buteo*) soaring in the clear skies above the wood. Ten years ago, you would have to travel west towards Dorset before you came across them but now they are a regular sight over Prickly Nut Wood. The increase in numbers and their 'migration' east may well be due to the gradual growth in organic farming methods in this region. The grassy ride into the larch plantation is alive with summer sounds. The warbling of the wood cricket (*Nemobius sylvestris*) and the hissing of the woodland grasshopper (*Omocestrus rufipes*) give the wood a tone reminiscent of tropical forests. The ride is dry and solid under foot, so the larch will be easy to extract. This plantation is known as a PAWS (*see previous two pages*).

With the larch extracted I mill up a number of 6 x 2 inch floor joists which are then notched into the roundwood larch floor supports. We take time over the joists, levelling and chiselling to ensure the work-shop floor can be trusted to form the base that many other projects will be constructed on. The floorboards are oak and chestnut and they have been seasoning 'in stick' for two years. I resaw the oak to remove the sapwood and begin to lay the floor.

The vigorous regrowth of the chestnut coppice is mirrored throughout the landscape. Arching branches of rambling roses, 'Paul's Himalayan Musk' and 'Bobbie James', are scenting the pergola beside the woodland house. In the vege-table garden we are coming to the end of our asparagus cut for the year and enjoying the new season's salads. Summer raspberries are beginning to ripen and the Japanese wineberries are being devoured by the children. The abundance of summer is just beginning. Tree flowers are forming and the lime flowers are beginning to open. Picked and dried they will make a refreshing tea, used for clarity of mind, relaxation and ease of sleep.

One of the colours that stands out when walking through chestnut coppice in early summer is the bright orange bracts of the sulphur polypore commonly known as 'chicken of the woods' (*Laetiporus sulphurus*). The reason for its name becomes apparent when it is cubed and cooked as a casserole, where the texture and flavour have an uncanny resemblance to chicken. However my favourite recipe is a freshly picked

## Ride Management

Rides and open glades within woodlands often develop a unique flora and fauna, different from the rest of the woodland. Rides create corridors through the woodland where sunlight can penetrate and therefore species selection may evolve differently. The woodland I work is predominantly sweet chestnut coppice and the ground flora is limited by the dense shade cast by the chestnut leaves, but the rides between the cants are covered with herbs and flowers and attract a wide range of butterflies. To enhance ride biodiversity, a system of cutting an ascending profile into the woodland allows more light to the grassy paths, and creates a shrub layer between the ride and the main woodland. Scalloping can also be used to break down the linear effect of straight rides.

**_Opposite left: Japanese wineberry._**

**_Opposite right: Emerging lime flowers._**

**_Above: A hammock under a scented 'Bobbie James' rose pergola is an ideal spot for a siesta on a hot day._**

## Chicken Tostado

A good sized specimen of chicken of the woods (*see below*) will feed many people. Choose the younger brightly coloured bracts as the pale yellowy/ white bracts will be tough and dry.

Large bract of chicken of the woods
Bread
1 tablespoon Olive oil
½ teaspoon tamari soy sauce
Garlic
1oz butter
Beefsteak tomato
1 teaspoon fresh basil – chopped

Rub garlic clove into freshly toasted bread. Mix olive oil and tamari and drizzle over toasted bread. Melt butter in large pan and fry thinly sliced chicken of the woods for a few minutes turning regularly, add sliced beefsteak tomato and chopped basil. Fry for a few minutes and serve on the toasted bread.

## Larch (*Larix decidua*)

A deciduous conifer introduced in 1625.

*Growing conditions:*
Needs frost free site and does best on well drained fertile soils.

*Silvicultural practice:*
Generally grown as a plantation crop, with regular thinnings to produce a final crop after 45-60 years. Being deciduous it can be useful in a continuous cover forestry system. Naturally fairly durable.

*Uses:*
Boat building
Boxes
Cladding
Fencing
Fibreboard
Floor joists
Gates
Pallets
Particle board
Pulp
Roof rafters
Roundwood timber framing
Rustic poles
Saw logs
Transmission poles

**_Above: Larch needles._**

**_Left: Larch in autumn prior to dropping its needles._**

# JUNE in a Lakeland Wood with Rebecca Oaks

simple lunch – chicken tostado.

I learnt the complex and multifaceted art of coppicing from the late Bill Hogarth MBE (1929-1999). Bill was the last coppice merchant in the Lake District to learn his trade from his father and from the 1980s he dedicated his time to passing on his skills and huge breadth of knowledge to many a young coppicing novice like me. So it is always with a powerful sense of continuity and reverence that I take to the Lakeland woods in late spring to practice oak bark peeling, one of Bill's favourite and most financially rewarding skills.

Many of the woods in south Lakeland are old oak coppices grown and cut over many generations on a 20 to 30 year cycle. For hundreds of years the timber went for charcoal production to fire furnaces for iron smelting. Oak was also in demand for swill basketmaking (*see bottom photo on page 98*) – a local speciality. Bill recalled a long history of his father sending peeled oak poles to rustic furniture makers in Cheshire and Manchester. Now we seem to have gone full circle and the timber will most likely be used for charcoal again, these days for barbecues. Oak bark however has always been in demand for tanning leather. At one time there were many local tanneries operating, now there are just one or two catering for a specialist market. Once peeled the bark is dried, then chopped and steeped in water in tan pits to release the tannins. Hides are left to soak in this liquor for many months. Leather produced from this process is of high quality, suitable for medical equipment.

When we first enter the wood to test whether the bark is lifting, there will likely be a carpet of bluebells under foot and a heady scent rising from the sun warmed banks. The bark will peel away most easily when the sap is flowing freely, tradition has it that May, June and July are peeling season. Interestingly, Bill noted that over the last fifty years he observed the bark peeling season gradually extending from mid April to late July – another sign, perhaps, of climate change.

By June, when the peeling is really well

***Top:* Rebecca Oaks.**

***Left:* Twiggy peeling oak bark.**

***Top right:* Peeled bark bundled ready for home.**

under way, the bluebells have faded and quickly die back leaving their leaves slimy and slick under foot; a treacherous prospect when carrying a long pole on one's shoulder. Soon the bursting oak leaves are going to cast a deep shade across the woodland floor and there are few plants that will thrive in these conditions.

Today I am cutting poles for a Scout troop tipi. The poles must be 20 feet long and no more than 3 inches wide at the base. Because this wood has quite dense growth the oak has tended to grow tall and slender so there are plenty of poles this size. However, I am little concerned as the thin poles do not have much 'crown' and you do need a good leafy top to draw the sap up freely. As a result some of the suppressed stems growing under the canopy often have bark that is 'sticky' and reluctant to let go. On this day, though, it turns out I need not be concerned once the pole is up onto the rack we have devised – two crossing oak posts lashed together with baler twine. The peeling iron slips under the bark and rips up smoothly along the length of the pole. With a twist of the wrist there is a satisfying sound as the bark slips off like peeling a banana. The question is how far can I go and still keep the bark in one piece? I have one proper peeling iron (borrowed off a colleague) with a pleasing weight, a slightly curved end and a comfy handle. But I can, just as easily and effectively, use our improvised tool fashioned from a piece of copper pipe flattened at one end.

With help from Twiggy, BHMAT apprentice (Bill Hogarth MBE Memorial Apprenticeship Trust), the finished pole is wrestled still slick with sap into an upright position leaning into one of the nearby trees, its beautiful pale nakedness as sinewy as a snake.

If left to stand, the poles will soon darken and often develop a sooty mildew which can detract from its appearance. Generally, the peeled poles weather to a silvery sheen and with the twists and natural forks used creatively they are fabulous for garden structures.

Today, there is little company in the woods. Any deer, of which there may well be a few, are lying low with their fawns still young and vulnerable. Some grey squirrels are chasing through the tops, lording it over these trees that once were the home of the more diminutive and native reds. I might just have to acquire a taste for spit roast squirrel and help to keep the numbers down. The chiffchaffs are vocal as ever, welcomed in spring as one of the first migrants to return; by June the song is wearisome in its insistence. More melodic are the garden warblers that lurk shyly in the denser thickets.

Our solitude is broken by a welcome visit from Mrs Booth, owner of these woods, who takes a keen interest in our coppicing work. Bill had his workshop at Black Beck which is part of her estate and it pleases her, I think, to see his work continuing even on this somewhat smaller scale.

Even now at the height of summer the sun disappears behind the dense larch trees higher up this north facing slope. Time to load the pick-up with the

## Oak Leaf Wine

Pick a gallon of young oak leaves in early June and pour a gallon of boiling water over the leaves and leave for 24 hours. Strain off the liquid and add 4lb of sugar and the grated rind of one lemon. Simmer for 30 minutes. When cool add wine yeast and the juice of three sweet oranges. Pour into a demijohn and insert air lock. Keep warm and allow to ferment until the bubbles no longer form. Siphon off and store in sealed jar in the cool for six months. Then rack off, bottle and cork, store for a further six months before drinking.

July

bundled bark and stack the hazardous slippery poles on top. Much strapping down and I'm ready for home, a hot bath and a glass of oak leaf wine.

July brings the heady hot days of an English summer and with it the peak demand for barbecue charcoal. I try and work with the weather at this time of year; up before the sun gets hot to unload the kiln, and then into the shade to make a chair or weave a seat. Then lunch and a siesta, a short nod in the hammock until the midday heat has reduced, and then reload the kiln and light early evening before lighting the home barbecue for dinner.

This morning has gone well, I unloaded the kiln before breakfast and I am now sitting in the shady retreat of my freshly completed roundwood workshop awaiting the arrival of participants for a Woodland and Permaculture Course. The build has gone smoothly and at last, after sixteen years, I have a level floor and something more substantial than a tarpaulin roof under which to convert and add value to the coppiced chestnut. It feels like the last piece of the jigsaw is in place, and the infrastructure is at last set up for successfully completing the whole process of converting a tree into finished product.

Seventy years ago, when these woods were tied to a working farm, there were barns where a woodsman could take produce to make a gate, or split chestnut laths in the dry. All the barns are now converted into domestic

dwellings and the farm no longer exists. So it has been necessary to create the infrastructure to make these woodlands viable again. I often think that the next woodsman in these woods will inherit house, workshop, on-cycle coppice and no rhododendron – I hope he or she appreciates it!

While considering these thoughts, my eye is drawn to a lizard, basking on a timber off-cut and I am quickly reminded of the diverse landscape and rich ecosystem I am fortunate to live in. The woodland is busy with lizards at this time of year. They bask on the woodpiles and rustle through the chestnut leaves in the more recently cut coppice.

My attention turns to the sound of voices, emerging up the ride, heading towards the clearing. I return to the outdoor kitchen to stoke the fire for tea.

After initial introductions, we take a walk through the woodland. The shade is welcome and we move slowly through the trees, stopping to discuss aspects of the management. We are making our way towards an area of woodland where we will be carrying out an observation exercise as part of a woodland assessment. Skullcap (*Scutellaria galericulata*) is prolific in flower along the ride edges, and the welcome sight of the white admiral (*Limentis camilla*) gliding towards us brings up discussions of life cycles and woodland management. Coppicing is of benefit to many butterflies and the caterpillar of the white admiral feed on the abundant honeysuckle growing up the coppice stems and across the woodland floor. The butterfly itself enjoys the bramble flowers that thrive on the edges of the woodland rides. Our joy at watching the antics of the white admiral is cut short by a 'yelp' from one of the participants who has been bitten by the 'silent injector' – the Cleg.

Clegs (*Haematopota pluvialis*) are the silent fast flying version of the horse fly and on humid days in midsummer can make their presence known. It is only

***July title page: Emperor dragonfly.***

***Left: The children's garden with photovoltaic array in background, part of the power supply to the woodland house.***

***Above: Newly completed workshop at Prickly Nut Wood.***

***Above right: White admiral.***

***Near right: Common lizard (*Lacerta vivipara*).***

***Far right: Skullcap.***

the female who bites to drink blood, the male feeds on nectar. We continue our walk, our focus of attention now transferred to what is flying around us rather than the woodland vegetation. The sight of an emperor dragonfly (*Anax imperator*) is most welcome and I reassure the group of its passion for eating clegs.

The participants split into pairs and spend the next half hour observing the woodland area I have found for them. I know this area of woodland well but another visit will bring up something new, hence the need for many visits to carry out a good assessment. I stress the need for visits day and night throughout the year. If an assessment on the woods was carried out only in winter, would the presence of white admirals have been noticed? And the need for honeysuckle and bramble for their life cycle. Without visiting at night during summer, it would be very hard to detect the presence of nightjars and the varieties of bats and moths that are so abundant in the woods.

We are hasty creatures, us humans, and we are keen to make a mark on the landscape. We forget sometimes that the woodland has been here for hundreds of years and seen many woodsmen come and go. Take your time when assessing a woodland. Visit the woodland as often as you can, see it through a woodland year before beginning any work.

We sit down under the shady canopy and receive feedback on what people have observed. How differently people see a woodland and what a benefit to have many minds and pairs of eyes observing. Permaculture principles advocate that 'more minds create more yield', in this case a wider range of views and understanding of a situation and therefore a better foundation on which to design a management strategy. I bring up this principle and share my enthusiasm for the diverse range of observations carried out in a very short time period.

I have visited this area regularly for the past eight years and have compiled observation records and species lists. I see it as a diverse and unique area of woodland amongst the chestnut coppice. It was once worked as a coppice with standards system: Oak over hazel with some ash and field maple as is common in many ancient woodlands in this area. The oaks have a fairly closed canopy and the hazel is being shaded out. Most foresters looking at this area would encourage the oaks by thinning and then aiming for a final crop in about fifty years time. The woodsman's approach is to recoppice the hazel, ash and field maple and give the oak a major thinning returning to a coppice with standards system. There would be enough oak for a small timber framed

***Top down, left column to right:***

***1. Self heal.***

***2. Enchanter's nightshade.***

***3. Silver washed fritillary butterfly.***

***4. Butcher's broom – the flowers are rarely noticed.***

***5. Hemp agrimony.***

***6. Bilberries.***

building from the oak thinning, so I would add value by converting the oak to a frame. I would need to layer the hazel to increase stocking rate and in this case deer fence the area as it is a good distance from my house and therefore not such a regularly visited area. This work would increase biodiversity and ensure another source of on-cycle hazel for hurdlemaking and hedgelaying.

We observe some of the visible flora within the woods and find an area of butcher's broom (*Ruscus aculeatus*), an ancient woodland indicator plant. The woodland edge throws up self heal (*Prunella vulgaris*), enchanter's nightshade (*Circaea lutetiana*) and hemp agrimony (*Eupatorium cannabinum*). More notes are taken and I encourage the participants to keep a monthly diary of plants seen within the woodland they are assessing.

The return walk back to the outdoor kitchen for lunch heralds a recent emergence of silver washed fritillary butterflies (*Argynnis paphia*). This butterfly is a regular sighting at Prickly Nut Wood as the coppicing provides the ideal habitat for the violets upon which the caterpillars of many fritillary butterflies feed. We watch for a while before continuing our walk, taking in the vigorous new stems of coppice

## Bilberry Pancakes

Bilberries are commonly found on acid soils, heathland and open clearings as well as ride edges in woods.

I make small pancakes with bilberries like a drop scone. The fruit is juicy and can be hot inside the pancake. This is a quick and simple recipe ideal for around the fire with delicious results.

*Pancake mixture*:
4 oz self raising flour
1oz caster sugar
1 cup milk
1 egg
Olive oil

Sift flour and mix with sugar in mixing bowl. Add egg and gradually cup full of milk beating with a wooden spoon. Use a heavy frying pan, and place over the fire. Add a little olive oil and then a tablespoon of batter for each pancake, keeping them apart. Add a few bilberries to each and when the bubbles rise through the pancakes, turn and cook other side.

## Yew (*Taxus baccata*)

Native conifer that will become the climax trees species on chalk downland. Our longest living native tree.

*Growing conditions*:
Slow growing, shade tolerant tree that will grow on most soils but most common on limestone and chalk.

*Silvicultural practice*:
Its shade tolerance makes it suitable for inclusion in continuous cover forestry. Can form pure stands of high forest as at Kingley Vale in West Sussex. Coppices well and has a distinct orange to purple heart-wood. Very durable and heavy in weight.

*Uses*:
Cabinets
Carving
Chairs
Fencing posts
Firewood
Furniture
Saw logs
Steam bending
Tables
Veneer

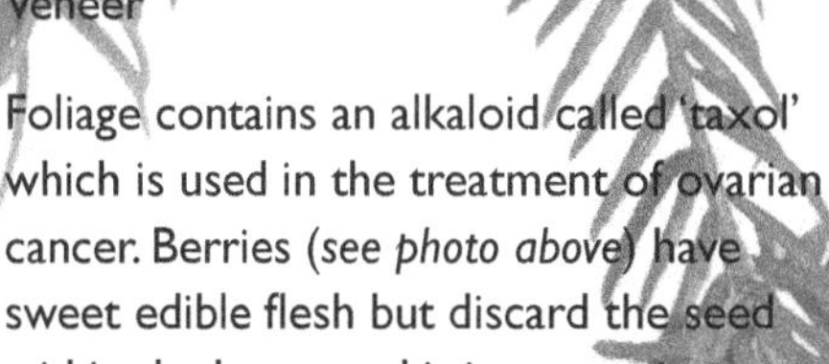

Foliage contains an alkaloid called 'taxol' which is used in the treatment of ovarian cancer. Berries (*see photo above*) have sweet edible flesh but discard the seed within the berry as this is very poisonous.

***Left: Ancient yews are often found in churchyards and abbey grounds like this one at Stedham Church, West Sussex.***

# JULY in Rawhaw Wood with Hugh & Carolyn Ross

regrowth from the winter's cut, and then making a climb over the greensand to collect bilberries (*Vaccinium myrtillus*) for a pancake lunch.

It's mid July, 2.30 in the morning and I'm up and about to check our charcoal kiln. The sky is very clear with lots of twinkling stars and a small sickle moon shining quite brightly, a slight breeze is blowing warm air up from the south west. Nothing much is stirring, just the occasional rustle of a small mammal moving around in the grass. Some nights it can be quite noisy, lots of animal sounds and traffic drone from the distant bypass.

We lit the kiln at 6.30 the previous evening and it's burning beautifully now. Smoke is gently rising from the chimneys and all four of them look to be puffing away at the same rate. The white smoke is slowly drifting away across the wheat field at the back of the wood. Shafts of orange heat radiate out from the inlet vents at the base of the kiln. It's such a warming sight, even at this time in the morning. But it's back to bed for now.

6.30 and the alarm clock rings. Carolyn climbs out of bed, it's her turn to check the kiln and put the kettle on. We will keep monitoring the kiln to make sure that it's burning properly, checking it every couple of hours through the morning and early afternoon and then more frequently when the burn nears its end. The way that the kiln burns tends to dictate our day. Sometimes you can almost light it and walk away, coming back twenty hours later to put it out. At other times it needs constant tweaking and attention to get it to burn evenly, and it can take up a great deal of time.

We return home from our morning dog walk just as Mick and Mark are arriving. We're building a timber framed house in the wood at the moment, and they are fixing wany edged cladding to the outside of the oak frame. Our work times are very haphazard, but the builders like to start drinking tea at 8.00 sharp. We discuss the day's work on the building and once everything is sorted we're off to cut wood.

We need to start processing wood for the next charcoal burn. We have an area set aside where we saw and split logs to usable lengths and size. It's well away from the smoking kilns. We have various group visits to the wood and we also use this area as a meeting place where we introduce ourselves and the wood to visitors.

Rawhaw Wood is 30 acres in size and has been designated a Site of Special

***Top: Hugh and Carolyn* Ross.**

***Left: Kiln burning well.***

***Top right: Hazel coppice regrowing beneath standards.***

***Below right: Hugh and Carolyn's woodland home.***

Scientific Interest (SSSI) by Natural England. It's classified as ancient semi-natural woodland. The earliest written record naming the wood dates back to 1299, when it was owned by an order of Cistercian monks who had an Abbey in Pipewell. By the evidence of the coppice stools we can also see that the wood has had a long history of coppice management.

Over the last 12 years we have reintroduced a hazel coppice rotation to the woodland and this has benefited the flora and wildlife within the wood. From early spring the whole place starts to come to life. By July, there's the heady scent of meadowsweet (*see meadowsweet wine recipe on next page*), its fluffy white cloud flowers humming with hovering flies, whilst the small blue/purple stars of self heal glint in the green mown rides. Insects are buzzing in the trees and grasses and the young

of a variety of birds and mammals are exploring their world.

Time to check the kiln again. It's still burning well, the smoke is beginning to thin, and has changed from white to light grey in colour.

After lunch Carolyn is going to carry on splitting wood and I'm off to make a couple of charcoal deliveries to local shops. We sell our charcoal through 25 outlets locally. This afternoon's deliveries are to a farm shop and an ironmonger.

I enjoy visiting the farm shops at this time of year as we can treat ourselves to homegrown strawberries and raspberries and stock up on fresh locally produced vegetables.

I arrive home just in time to help Carolyn close down the kiln at the end of the burn. The smoke has thinned to a light blue fume and now smells like a barbecue rather than woodsmoke. We seal the air inlets to starve the fire of oxygen, and remove and seal the chimneys. We will leave the kiln to cool for 48 hours before we can unload and bag the charcoal.

We have one last job to do today before we finish work. Tomorrow I'm doing a charcoal burning display in a nearby country park, and we have to load up the car and trailer ready for the morning. We have a small portable kiln and a couple of display boards. One shows the charcoal process and the second tells people about Rawhaw Wood, our woodland management and also about the Rockingham Forest. Rockingham forest is an area of pasture and woodlands established by William the Conqueror as a royal hunting forest. It also has a long history of charcoal making which fuelled iron smelting in the area.

I enjoy doing these events as it allows me to talk directly to members of the public and to promote the benefits of using British charcoal. Environmentally, because most is made using coppiced hardwoods from local woodlands, it actually benefits our wildlife. It also reduces transport miles, and its superior quality means it is much easier to light and needs no lighter fuels, so your food is not tainted by chemical solvents. We take bags of charcoal to sell, plus other coppice products such as items of rustic furniture, stick pencils and drawing charcoal sticks.

It's a pleasant warm evening, so we're sitting out on the porch. We've some minted lamb chops to barbecue with salad and couscous, followed by strawberries and cream, and a beer while we're cooking.

The light is just beginning to diminish and bats are already flitting through the canopy of the oak trees. The daytime creatures are settling into their night time routines, we hear the last calls of pheasants and

## Meadowsweet Wine

1 gallon meadowsweet flowers
1lb dried raisins
1kg (2.2 lbs) sugar
1 large cup strong black tea
3 lemons
Water
Wine yeast

Place the flowerheads, sugar and raisins into a fermenting bin and pour over boiling water to dissolve sugar. Make up to a gallon with water and, when blood temperature, add juice of lemons, black tea and yeast. Keep covered and stir twice daily for five days. Strain off the pulp into a demijohn and fit airlock. Rack as necessary, bottle when fermentation is complete and drink young.

# AUGUST

# AUGUST in Prickly Nut Wood

blackbirds and then... stillness and quiet.

**_Left: Hugh inspecting hazel with a view to the next cut._**

**_Right: Sensible clothes for bagging up._**

August brings a break for me in the woodland year. It is around this time I usually take a family holiday and head down to my favourite beach in Devon, leaving my friend and fellow woodsman, Crispin, to look after the woods in my absence. When you live within a woodland and spend almost every day interacting in one form or another with trees, a holiday spent on the beach looking out towards the horizon with no trees in sight is therapeutic and restful, but after a week or so I begin to miss the woods and feel eager to return under the canopy.

While on the beach, I try to make the most of the maritime harvest. On good years, the beach provides an abundance of food and on others I can scratch around coming away with just a handful of prawns and a pollock. If the tide is right, when the sand eels come into the bay, the mackerel are there in numbers and half an hour with a rod and feathers can provide plenty of fish for family and friends. Fresh caught mackerel, gutted and then cooked on the barbecue with a little butter and black pepper while the waves roll in and claw at the beach is to me a simple taste of paradise and I know I am on holiday. There are few fish that match up to mackerel when barbecued fresh but the predator that chases the mackerel is one such fish, the sea bass. My brother Dan is the bass catcher amongst us and seems to have a sixth sense that somehow ensures he chooses the right lure for the right occasion. That and he spends a lot more time with a line in the water than I do ensures if there's bass to be caught, he will catch them. I have often netted good-sized prawns around the rocks and we have picked up some tasty crabs in pots we have set out by the rocks. Of course there is plenty of time for swimming, sand castles and beach cricket but the opportunity for wild food always calls me wherever I am located.

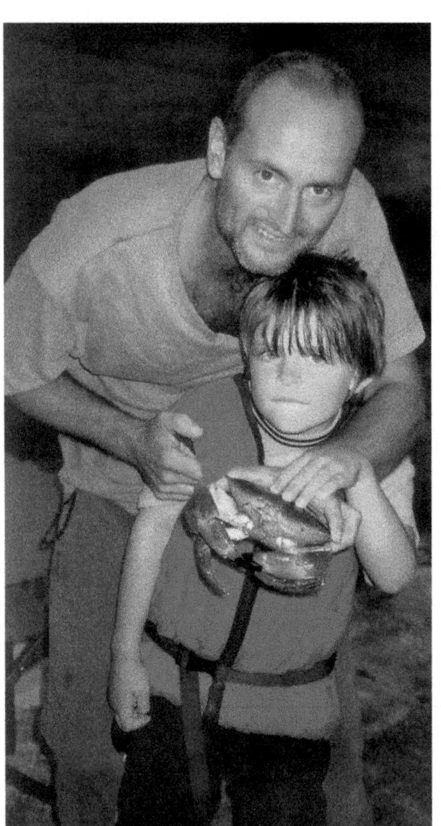

**_August title page: Gone fishing._**
**_Left: Crabbing with Rowan._**
**_Above: Productive meditation._**
**_Below: Barbecueing mackerel back at the cottage._**

**_Above: With Oily overlooking the bay._**

**_Below: Brother Dan barbecuing mackerel on the beach with Prickly Nut Wood charcoal._**

Back from my holiday and I am greeted with an urgent shingle order. Fortunately I have left a good number of shingle blanks ready for splitting out as most years I either receive an order or have a building project that needs shingling.

There are two types of shingle, those that are milled and those that are split. Most milled shingles are made from western red cedar, but milled oak and sweet chestnut are sometimes available. The western red cedar shingles that are for sale in most roofing merchants are imported from the USA and Canada incurring high timber miles. Fortunately, more local woodsmen are now using their sawmills to convert western red cedar into shingles. This is a great way to add value to thinnings and create a local building material in the process.

Split shingles are usually made from oak and sweet chestnut. Most are radially split, like cutting segments out of a round cake. I have made some shingles this way but most I make are known as 'bastard' shingles. These can be made out of smaller diameter pieces of wood than the radially cleaved shingles and are therefore very suited to sweet chestnut coppice. I take a round blank about 12 inches long and between 5-8 inches in diameter. Using a froe, I square off the sides to remove the sapwood and then continue to split out the square removing the very central piece which is liable to split. I then drawknife a slight taper and bevel the end grain on the thicker exposed edge. These hand cleaved and crafted shingles are obviously more expensive than the sawn alternative but their lack of uniformity adds character and brings a building alive. Being cleaved rather than sawn, they will be stronger and more durable and there will be less cut fibres for the rainwater to penetrate. The order is for a small structure, only 3,000 required. I estimate it will take me three weeks.

To break up my shingle making I take walks to delight in the abundance of soft fruit available around the house at this time of year. The children have consumed nearly all the Japanese wineberries (*Rubus phoenicolasius*) but I find a few on the higher stems and mixed with the abundance of wild strawberries, autumn raspberries, the last of the plums, and damsons, it doesn't take a long walk to enjoy a fruit salad straight from the bush before returning to my shingle making.

Many products made in the wood

***Below left: Squaring up a shingle blank.***

***Below right: Splitting out bastard shingles.***

such as shingles, laths and pales could be seen as monotonous work, but once you get 'into the zone' of what you are making, many a pleasant day can be spent making these products. It is summer and the workload is light and creative, far removed from the physicality of a winter's day. I avoid counting as I work, it doesn't make the product appear any quicker. I steadily produce the product and at the end of a few days, I am usually pleasantly surprised by the number of bundles stacked up. Of course with all this conversion of timber to finished product, there is always a good pile of peelings or shavings or sawdust. These are a by-product of my work and once dried out are used as kindling to light the many fires used in woodland life. In the same way the planer peelings end up as chicken bedding, the chicken manure is then composted for the vegetable garden and the chickens spend the winter weeding and manuring the fruit cage. The sawdust from the sawmill goes to the compost toilet and the composted contents of the toilet end up around the fruit trees. I eat the fruit from the fruit trees and the cycle begins again. Cycles within cycles, everything has a use within this cyclical lifestyle in the woodland year.

***Above left:***
***Laying out shingles prior to side axe and draw knife work.***

***Above right:***
***The end result – cleft chestnut roofing shingles.***

***Left:***
***Fixing local western red cedar sawn shingles on a roundwood timber frame building in Sussex.***

After I have harvested all the plums and damsons, I prune the trees. This year the volume of damsons has enticed me back with boxes for an evening picking to make jam and wine for the winter months ahead. It is late August now and that means late summer. The nights have been slowly drawing in for the past two months and although the days are still hot, something is telling me it is time to begin harvesting and storing for the winter ahead. It is a feeling I get, I just know it's time. At the end of winter, there is an urgency to complete the coppicing and extraction before springburst. Then spring arrives and I feel part of it and I grow with it into summer. Summer's pace is easy going and thoughts of the following winter are far from my mind until now. Like the nightjars in the wood who are getting ready to migrate, I am preparing for winter. I wonder whether they experience the same knowing feeling as I do? In the same way? On the same day? I will never know but I like to think that around this time this woodland ecosystem of which I am part has a seasonal consciousness that I am picking up on.

Winter food is scarce and the more that is stored through drying, bottling

# Western Red Cedar (*Thuja plicata*)

Evergreen conifer introduced into Britain in 1854.

*Growing conditions:*
A shade bearer which tolerates alkaline soils and is moderately frost hardy.

*Silvicultural practice:*
Usually grown as a dense plantation but is better suited in continuous cover forestry where its shade tolerance can be used. Occasionally used as a nurse tree. Light weight timber.

***Top: Western red cedar foliage.***

***Middle: Clean trunk for milling.***

***Bottom: Closeup of bark.***

*Uses:*
Bark for seating and other artefacts
Chipboard
Cladding
Fencing
Fibreboard
Firewood
Greenhouses
Joinery
Ladders
Posts
Pulpwood
Rails
Roundwood timber framing
Rugby goal posts
Scaffold poles
Seed boxes
Sheds
Shingles
Weatherboarding

## Damson Jam

2½lb damsons
3lb sugar
¾ pint water

Wash damsons and slit skins. Put a preserving pan on the stove and add damsons and water and simmer until the damsons soften. At this stage use a 'holy' spoon to remove as many stones as you are able then add sugar and continue on low heat, stirring until sugar has dissolved. Bring to the boil, stirring frequently as it thickens until it reaches setting point. Stones not removed earlier will surface now for removal. Pot and seal in hot sterile jam jars.

## Damson Wine

5lb damsons
3lb sugar
1 gallon water
Yeast

Crush damsons in fermenting bucket and add the sugar. Boil water and pour over damsons. Stir to dissolve sugar and allow to cool to blood temperature before adding yeast. Cover and leave for three days before straining through sieve or muslin into dark demijohns. Fit airlock and rack regularly. Bottle when fermentation is complete in dark bottles.

***Left: Comma butterfly enjoying ripe damsons at Prickly Nut Wood.***

# AUGUST in The Wood with Paul Morton & Jo Callaghan

and pickling, the more it will ensure that in the depths of winter the tastes of summer can reappear, giving encouraging thoughts of the seasons to come and easing the hard work of winter.

I am a woodsman. Three years ago I was employed as a factory worker on shifts, making jam. Now, I am self-employed and earning my living from 38 acres of woodland which I own and manage. This has been the most challenging, rewarding, enriching and wonderful change of my life.

Woodland life and crafts can have a romantic quality that draws people from more conventional ways of life, including me. The romance of it attracted me briefly but I soon learned of the gritty hard work involved. Hard work has never put me off. It was not just attraction that drew me; it was a basic, raw need, which drove me, almost compulsively to this complete change of being.

Committing myself to this way of life means that I have had to take on board a huge range of new skills and resources. I have learnt (and am still learning) the skills of cleaving, shaving, felling, chopping, carving and weaving so I can make a living from the wood. I am continuously observing and learning about the life of the birds, mammals, insects, plants and fungi in order to be able to think ahead and plan for the good of the whole woodland ecosystem. This is a responsibility I do not take lightly. Conservation is always my guiding principle and business needs come second. Life has become rich with a diversity of tasks and activities in the wood that change throughout the year from season to season.

So during August in our woods my main activity is harvesting wych elm bark. The inner bark of wych elm is a fantastic material for weaving because of its flexible nature. It will weave around the seat rail of a chair without breaking. The inner bark has a pattern which looks very attractive when it is dried and woven into a seat.

The process begins with felling the tree sometime in the spring or summer. This is the period when new wood cells are forming, creating a moist layer underneath the bast (inner bark), which allows it to be removed easily. I leave the felled tree where it is and strip the bark immediately. First I use a drawknife to remove the outer bark so that the bast is exposed. Then using a sharp knife I cut strips approximately 1¼ inches wide following the length of the tree along the grain and avoiding knots and branches. I pull the bast off in these long strips, marking the length to the nearest 0.5 metre once it is coiled up. The bark can be woven straight away or dried for use later in the year when it will be soaked in hot water to make

***Top:** Paul Morton and Jo Callaghan.*

***Left:** Cleft chestnut gate in progress.*

***Top right:** Stored coils of hanging wych elm bark.*

***Far right:** Cedar bark backpack.*

it flexible again. I hang the coils of bark on poles to dry over the wood burner. They look and smell wonderful. Once dried they will store indefinitely, as long as they are kept hung up and dry.

Over the last twenty to thirty years it has become a popular material for weaving a seat into post and rail chairs and stools. I sell it to other green woodworkers for chairmaking and this provides me with a steady income throughout the summer. It is a great feeling of satisfaction to be harvesting and utilising another part of the tree.

The felled trees will, of course, grow from the stumps and can be harvested again in 14 - 20 years. There are both wych elm and English elm in the wood, though the stripped bark is from wych elm. Dutch Elm Disease has left many dead trees in the wood and put at risk the colony of white-letter hairstreak butterfly which are dependant on elm. There is an unusually large colony of these threatened butterflies in the wood. The 14 - 20 year rotation will ensure that the tree has the best chance to survive Dutch Elm Disease, as it is older trees that are more susceptible, but they will still grow large enough for the white-letter hairstreak butterfly colony.

This August, as an experiment, I fell a western red cedar which has a wonderful outer bark, a deep reddish brown. The cedar was introduced from North America. Native Americans used the bark to weave baskets, boxes and other containers. A friend of ours began experimenting with the bark and has become passionate about its beauty and strength, she makes sculptures which are moulded or left to take on their own unique form as the bark dries, curls and hardens. She came to the wood in August and stripped a large sheet of bark and made a beautiful cedar bark backpack.

I wanted to try using the inner bark for weaving into chair seats. I had never done this before but decided to try the same techniques that I used for wych elm. I stripped off the outer bark with my drawknife. This needed more care because the inner bark is thinner than wych elm. The inner bark of cedar is pale pink, turning orangey red immediately it is exposed to the air. To test its flexibility I bent the strip in half but the fibres frayed, then I wound it round my finger which is the approximate dimension of a seat rail – this was more successful, and seeing it had potential I stripped the whole tree. When I dried it in coils it turned a nice deep red.

I have made lots of chair seats with wych elm bark and I know its strengths. Cedar bark was an unknown so I decided to make a seat in the same way to see what happens during the weaving process, as it dries and then how it stands up to use over time.

After it was woven and dried I found that the cedar seat was more brittle than wych elm so I rubbed in oil to soften it.

Any bark woven chair needs to be kept indoors in dry conditions as damp air can cause the bark to go mouldy. Cedar wood is naturally very rot resistant. I have found the bark is too. The stool I made using the cedar bark is kept outside undercover in my workshop and does not show signs of mould. As it has aged the colour has really darkened – it is almost black. If it had been kept indoors it may have kept its deep red colour.

I also spend some of August working in someone else's woods nearby. This came about three years ago when I was working in the jam factory and owning woodland seemed just a crazy dream. I booked myself onto a green woodworking course in Herefordshire. This was an introductory course set in a small private woodland. I met some great people and they, along with the woodland and the course itself, were very inspirational. I returned a week or so later to help build a clay oven in the woods for the course kitchen. I offered to help out as a volunteer on other courses over the summer and the tutor agreed. In return for helping in the kitchen, chopping wood, keeping the kiln fires going and other odd jobs I was able to use the equipment and some wood to try making traditional green wood furniture. I learned the basic green woodworking skills of pole lathing, cleaving and shaving wood and came away with a small three legged stool and a ladder back side chair, as well as being one step closer to my dream of owning and working my own wood.

***Above: Paul teaching elm bark weaving.***

***Right: Jo training with Hercules.***

Now I work as an assistant on these courses throughout the summer and in August I assisted on two chairmaking courses. I also supply wych elm bark for students and teach them how to weave a seat into the chair that they have made.

I mow the rides and glades during July and August. I use a scythe for this task which makes it hard work. But it is very satisfying to hear the swish of the scythe amid the quiet peace of the woods.

I rake off the cuttings so that they do not rot down and fertilise the soil. This promotes a more diverse ground vegetation encouraging wild flowers that need a poor quality soil. These permanent open areas in woodland are important for grassland flowers and associated butterflies and other invertebrates.

Jo is an artist and uses the beauty of the woods as her inspiration. Last August she was captivated with the patterns created by the light in the woods and the different shapes of leaves and grasses. She created pieces that she placed around the wood at the edges of the glades so that they would catch the wind and the light. They evoked a lot of interest from walkers in the woods.

There is a heavy horse centre based in some woods near us. The horses work in the woods extracting timber, moving tools, bracken bashing and scarifying land for regeneration. This method of working the wood fascinates me. It is more natural than bringing in machines; it has a lower impact on the woods and fits with my policy of using hand tools and traditional ways of working as much as possible. So I booked on a week's horse logging course. Having no experience with horses I was very wary of them at first, but soon learned to trust their gentle ways and good training. It was a great week and I learned a lot and decided I definitely wanted a horse of my own to work in our wood.

Hercules was given to us on long-term loan along with a full harness, a swingle tree and a bag of feed. He was initially kept at the heavy horse centre for three months and during this period we learnt to work him under supervision and become familiar with horse logging equipment and techniques. So twice a week throughout August, Jo and I would go to the centre, catch Hercules, groom and harness him, ready for half an hour's training. We spent time schooling him and practising pulling spruce logs down steep muddy slopes to the woodpile. We learned to negotiate difficult ground while at the same time driving the horse and making sure the logs did not bash into any of the standing trees, or us, and line them up next to each other (fairly) neatly.

Next August Hercules will be working in our wood, pulling out the felled and stripped elm logs, to be seasoned for our winter wood store.

A few Augusts ago I was working in the repetitive environment of a jam factory. Now, every day, week and month is different. The wood constantly creates new interest and activities. I wake up looking forward to the day's work in the open air surrounded by all the different sounds, smells and sights of woodland life.

SEPTEMBER

# SEPTEMBER in Prickly Nut Wood

with fruit from who knows where. The jam I make now is made with fruit gathered from the woods and nothing tastes better.

September mornings trigger another message of change and encroaching winter. Although usually a mild month here in the south and often filled with sunlit days, the nights are drawing in quickly now and the mornings wet with dew. September is my window in the year when my wood-based tasks are at a minimum which is fortunate as the yields of wild and cultivated food demand much attention. It is also the time I take stock and reflect back over the summer now departing and begin to consider which cants I may be cutting come November.

September is also the time I interview for apprentices and know that I will have to disappoint as well as please with the decisions I have to make.

On this perfect September morning I set out for the day, backpack for, water to drink and food I plan to find upon the way. The field to the north-east is magically spun with silken spider threads. Enhanced by the morning dew and the low rising sun, I enter an enchanted landscape. Spider populations will be at their height at this time of year, (it can be millions to the acre) and they will move to new pastures if they become overcrowded. By spinning a silvery thread and floating on the end of this, they are carried by the wind to their new location.

My walk takes me through a shelterbelt which I planted fifteen years ago. The trees are now well established and I notice some 'wilding' apples standing out with a bright red sheen. A 'wilding' is a pip grown apple and will not remain true to the apple the pip was taken from. Cross pollination will ensure an apple of unknown lineage and may or may not be good to eat. This 'wilding' has a pleasant taste not dissimilar to a variety I grow called 'Idared'. I pick a few for my walk and notice the 'marble galls' on many of the oak trees in the shelterbelt. Galls are growths formed by the tissues of the tree caused by another organism,

***September title page: Acorns of* Quercus robur.**

***Left: Red 'wilding' apples in the shelterbelt.***

***Above: Marble gall on* Quercus robur.**

***Opposite top left:* Boletus *– penny bun.***

***Opposite top right: Beefsteak fungus.***

***Near right: Onions and garlic drying before being strung for winter storage.***

n this case the gall wasp (*Andricus kollari*). The gall provides shelter and food for one emale who will leave the gall any time now. There are 90 species of gall wasp in the Britain and 42 of these create galls on oak trees.

I continue my walk and cut across the common, an area of ancient wood pasture. Old oaks stand above the newer growth of blackthorn, hazel and sallow. My eye catches the familiar sight of the penny bun (*Boletus edulis*), a popular feast amongst most mushroom eaters, I pick a dozen for lunch and continue on my way.

Circling around towards the house I am back amidst the familiar chestnut coppice and spy a beefsteak fungus (*Fistulina hepatica*) on an old chestnut stump. This is an interesting fungus as it has a relationship with oak which causes the timber to discolour to a pleasing shade of brown. This brown oak fetches a premium price as it is sought after by furniture makers. Beefsteak is good eating and gets its name from its appearance when sliced as it would be hard at a glance to distinguish it from a slice of steak.

## Mushroom Forage Lunch

I made this with ceps and beefsteak but this simple recipe is adaptable to whatever edible wild mushrooms you may find. It is a perfect campfire recipe and ensures they are eaten fresh.

I pint of wild edible mushrooms
I onion
2 cloves garlic
Splash of Olive oil
Seasoning
Salt and pepper
Lemon juice
Teaspoon chopped fresh parsley

Heat a heavy pan on the fire, add olive oil and fry finely chopped onion and garlic for a couple of minutes turning regularly. Trim, clean and slice the mushrooms and add to pan. Fry for a few minutes, turning regularly, add a squeeze of lemon juice and finish with fresh parsley. Serve on top of toast, preferably spread with surplus juices and oil from the pan.

## Elderberry Wine

There are many recipes for elderberry wine and rightly so as it makes the closest wine in flavour to a red grape wine. I have stuck with this recipe as it is not as sweet or as a heavy on alcohol as some, but ensures the flavour of the elderberry shines through.

3lb elderberries
2½ lbs sugar
1 gallon water
Yeast

Remove the berries from their stalks into the fermenting bucket and crush them. (I use a 2 inch diameter coppice pole) Pour boiling water on to them. Let it cool to blood temperature before adding the yeast. Stir twice daily and after three days strain through a muslin or fine sieve over sugar. Pour the liquid into dark glass demijohns (or wrap clear demijohn with brown paper) to keep colour. Do not fill to the top and plug with cotton wool until vigorous initial ferment has occurred. Then top up and fit air lock. When fermentation is complete, bottle and try to leave for a year!

## Rowanberry Wine

This unique flavoured wine is an old favourite of mine. I buy wheat flakes from the local health food store, any surplus make a good breakfast.

3lb rowan berries
1lb raisins, chopped
1lb flaked wheat
3lb sugar
1 gallon water
2 lemons
Yeast

Remove the berries from their stalks into the fermenting bucket and pour boiling water over them, cover and let it stand for five days. Strain liquid and add sugar, flaked wheat, raisins and juice of lemons. Stir until sugar has dissolved and add yeast, cover with tea towel and leave to ferment. Stir daily and then after two weeks strain through a muslin or sieve into a demijohn. Fit air lock and leave to ferment, racking as necessary. Bottle once fermentation has ended. Drink young.

I add it to my bounty and continue my loop back to the outdoor kitchen. Bev has been laying out onions and garlic to dry and I take a sample of each and light the fire. It is not long before the smell of ceps (penny buns) and beefsteak are wafting through the woods.
After lunch I go harvesting small berries. Both elderberries (*Sambucus nigra*) and rowan berries (*Sorbus aucuparia*) make fine wines. They are a little fiddly to prepare as after picking the clusters of berries they need to be removed from the stalks with a fork into the fermentation bucket.

Another glorious September morning with the dew heavy once more and today I am walking into the village to collect cobnuts from the small platt (nut orchard) I manage there. Today I take the high road, up the hill and then the descent through Paul's farm and into the village. It is a favourite walk of mine as the South Downs are constantly in view and I am above the woods where I live and work. This gives me a different perspective and helps me in my ongoing process of observation of the landscape. As I begin the climb out of the woods it is not butterflies I encounter on the rides but caterpillars. These are moth caterpillars, first the grey dagger (*Acronicta psi*) with its distinctive yellow stripe and then amongst the partially devoured willow herb, I encounter the distinctive elephant hawk moth caterpillar (*Deilephila elpenor*) named in account of its trunk-like mouth shape.

Past the farm, I check up on an old walnut tree that overhangs the footpath and collect a good bag full of nuts. The outer cases colour my hands with their yellow/green stain, they make an excellent clothes dye.

It is not long before I am standing amongst the cob nuts. It is a bountiful harvest and I fill the two boxes I have with me in no time and have to flag down a passing car in the village street to help transport my harvest home.

For me September conjures up childhood memories of blackberrying. We used to walk up the lane which merged into a footpath bisecting arable fields carrying old quart milk churns. My brother Dan and I, like most children, filled our bellies before we started collecting berries to take home. Faces and clothes stained with blackberry juice, hands and wrists scratched and sore, we would return with our quart of blackberries to be turned into one of Britain's culinary delights, blackberry and apple crumble. A September blackberry and apple crumble with fresh picked blackberries and apples straight from the tree is an essential part of the woodland year.

When woodlands are coppiced, brambles often appear. This vigorous plant is part of a woodland's natural defence. A freshly formed bramble thicket will usually contain coppice re-growth or naturally regenerated trees growing up protected from browsing animals by its impenetrable spikes. The brambles whose outreaching stems grabbed at my bootlaces in May are now providing me with nutrition as I fill my churn with berries. As the woodland grows and the canopy closes, the blackberries will be shaded out and slowly retreat from the woodland flora, colonising the edges of rides and woodland clearings instead.

Late September and I am busying

***Top left:***
***Grey dagger caterpillar.***

***Bottom left:***
***Elephant hawkmoth caterpillar.***

***Right:***
***Author with box of cobnuts.***

## Blackberry & Apple Crumble

½lb blackberries
1lb cooking apples (my favourite is 'Annie Elizabeth')
2oz sugar

*For the crumble*:
6oz wholewheat flour
2oz rolled oats
4oz soft brown sugar
3oz butter
1 level teaspoon baking powder

Peel and slice the apples into baking dish, then add blackberries and sugar. Place flour and oats in mixing bowl, add baking powder and then rub butter into the flour lightly with your fingers. Once it is well rubbed in add sugar and mix in well. Sprinkle crumble mixture over the fruit and bake for 30 minutes at 350°F (180°C).

Serve with fresh cream or yoghurt.

myself with sorting firewood for the winter. The Rayburn I run primarily on sweet chestnut, saving most other hardwoods for the open fire. When you supply logs as a product to others, you are often left with the 'gleanings'. In other words the best quality driest seasoned wood is delivered to customers and I am left to split out the gnarly, twisted grain pieces at the bottom of the pile. At least that's how it was for a number of years but I now have a well organised log shed and make certain I have a good supply of split wood undercover, but I still make use of the gnarly pieces as they are slow burning and help to ensure the Rayburn stays in overnight.

I find September a good time for maintenance around the homestead in the woods. There are always posts that need replacing, raised beds to construct, windows that need oiling and fencing and gates to make and erect. We have made do with an old pallet on a rope for the past couple of years for a gate into the garden and a decent gate is well overdue. I select a couple of poles from my chestnut pile for the 'harr' and 'slammer' and create a flat face on three sides, leaving one in the round. This is my pattern for when I make chestnut gates, the outer edges are left in the round. I chisel out the mortises and leave

a slight jowl on the top rail to reduce the risk of the gate dropping. I hang the finished gate on a round chestnut post with a Sussex 'oigg' as a cap and work in some cleft post and rail and some small diameter criss-cross trellis between the latch post and the veranda.

## Ash (*Fraxinus excelsior*)

Native tree often found in ancient woodland in association with field maple and hazel.

*Growing conditions:*
Likes deep calcerous soils and will grow as a pioneer species in these conditions. Prefers sheltered aspect.

*Silvicultural practice:*
Coppices well and naturally regenerates abundantly. Grown as a timber tree on 60-80 year rotation, regular thinning is recommended.

***Top right: The light foliage of ash creates a dappled shade.***

***Middle: Coppiced ash.***

***Bottom: The smooth bark of ash turns fissured as it ages.***

*Uses:*
Barrel hoops
Boats
Bows
Chairs
Charcoal
Crates and lobster pots
Firewood
Floor boards
Furniture
Gates
Gate hurdles
Hay rakes
Joinery
Ladders
Oars
Pickle from ash keys
Pulpwood
Rail
Saw logs
Shafts
Spears
Sports equipment
Steam bending
Tent pegs
Tool handles
Turnery
Veneers
Walking sticks
Yurts

# SEPTEMBER in Brookhouse Wood with Mike Abbott

It takes me to finish the gate to realise that there are three more I need to make.

***Above: Cleft chestnut gate.***

For most creatures that live in the northern hemisphere, September is a time to gather in the harvest in order to survive the winter. My harvesting consists of running the last block of woodland courses which are my major source of income and September is an ideal time. It can often be warm and dry but without the oppressive heat and the accompanying insects that can afflict July and August. Although the days are still longer than the nights, the rapidly decreasing daylight means that work has to finish early enough for sociable evenings around the campfire. The brambles that are such a curse during the rest of the year, now compensate by yielding their soft juicy blackberries. Apples abound in the orchards while damsons are dripping from the hedges. All in all, it's a good time to be out in the woods.

I started running green woodwork courses in 1985 moving every couple of years between various woodlands around the south-west of England. After ten itinerant years I fulfilled a long standing dream and bought a share in a 10 acre woodland in Herefordshire together with my wife, Tamsin, and five other woodland enthusiasts. We renamed the woodland after the local Victorian chairmaker, Philip Clissett, and here I shared a workshop with fellow green woodworker, Gudrun Leitz. After ten years in the same place, having to make the inevitable compromises demanded by a co-operative venture, I felt the need to move on and have a workshop to myself again. So in 2005 I sold my share in Clissett Wood and moved my workshop to a farm woodland a few miles along the valley from our cottage.

I rent the space for my workshop from an enterprising farmer whose 300 acre farm contains ten acres of ancient woodland plus about 30 acres of new woodland that he has planted over the last 20 years. My annual rent consists of 100 hours of woodland work usually carried out between New Year and Easter. This consists mainly of thinning out the trees of lesser quality to enable the better ones to grow on. I then sort out the straightest and least knotty logs along with any useful forks and tripods for use on the courses. The remainder is then used as firewood mostly for the farm, but also for the courses and for our home.

September 2007 started with a six-day greenwood chairmaking course. My assistant was Rich Bates, a

***Top: Mike Abbott.***

***Left: Richard Bates (second from left) assisting on six day chairmaking course.***

young man in his early 30s who had spent the previous winter working alongside Ben Law at Prickly Nut Wood. As usual, the course started after lunch with introductions, a safety talk and a tour of the site with the students (I don't think this is quite the right word – they are not on my courses to study but to experience – but it's the best word I can think of).

Although I still had a stock of logs, felled during the previous spring, I like to have some really fresh wood as well, so the next thing was to fell a cluster of coppiced ash stems. To enable everyone to go home with a finished chair, we had to follow a fairly tight schedule. After the first day of practising the new techniques, they then had to spend the second day cleaving and shaving the side rungs and rails, then cleave, shave and steambend the back legs. This allows two nights and a day for the rungs to dry in our woodfired drying box and for the bend on the back legs to set to shape.

Day three was spent making the various front and back components for the chairs depending on what style of chair they were making, be it ladder-back, spindle-back or lath-back. More steam-bending was needed, so Rich had his time cut out keeping the steamer boiling as well as keeping the kettles on the boil for hot drinks, not to mention giving advice and assistance to the students. The uninitiated would think that most of the work was done by the end of day three. However the students now encountered a whole new range of skills to enable them to spend the next two days assembling their chairs.

The first thing was to take the rungs out of the dryer and measure precisely the diameter of the tenons (the ends of the rungs that fit into the holes drilled into the legs of the chairs). These tenons will have been shaped while the wood was still green. This was done either by using a sizing tool on the pole-lathe or by using a very handy device called a tenon cutter. This is a modern piece of equipment which can be fitted into a hand-brace (as in a brace-and-bit) or into a cordless drill (we have no mains electricity on site). While in the dryer, the tenons had shrunk by a predictable amount to a slightly oval shape. The students then drilled the correct sized holes into the chair legs and then, using a powerful sash cramp, they squeezed the chair frame together. By taking advantage of the way the wood warps and shrinks as it dries, a strong frame can be created without the need for any glue.

By the end of day four all the students had the side panels of their chairs assembled while the back and front components remained in the drying box. It then took all of day five to drill, shape and assemble the remainder of their chairs. For those that followed the schedule, day six was spent applying a woven seat. However, as always happens, people wanted to do their individual thing and with most of the students having attended previous courses, they had the skills to push on with a few other projects. Frankie was desperate to make a stand for a small side table, so she stripped the bark off a tripod which had been growing in the top of one of the coppice stems. She was so pleased with this that she made a second one. Anthea had recently become a grandmother and decided to make a high-chair. This required a sharper bend than usual which resulted in some splitting on the crown of the bend but with some delicate shaving and careful drilling the chair went together beautifully. Marian wanted to reseat the chair she had made last time, so she brought that along as well.

Phil was another regular on the courses

***Left:** Group photo at end of chairmaking course.*

***Above right:** Bow making course.*

***Right:** Firing the bows.*

and he decided to knock out a couple of basic ladder-back chairs but to seat them when he got home. As a novice to green woodwork, Rob was undaunted and succeeded in producing a fine armchair. He had been staying with his wife at the local bed and breakfast, so when she arrived to collect him from the woods, she was able to help him weave a hemp rope seat after the group photo. Roger decided to take it easy and made a bar stool with a single back slat, which he finished with an innovative weave out of seagrass. When each student left, they took with them far more than a wooden chair. They had all spent a week making real contact with the woodland in a way which far surpasses the experience that can be gained from a simple walk in the woods. During the following fortnight, Rich and I guided another dozen or so people through two similar greenwood courses.

Over the previous winter we had spent several winter weekends in the woods with our two children together with some of their friends who brought along their parents. Inevitably we started messing about making bows and arrows. One thing leads to another, so we planned a weekend course in September with an experienced bowmaker, Peter Whiteman. Peter duly arrived with a dozen lengths of ash that he had been drying for several months.

This provided me with a great oppor-tunity to escape from the workshop and to work in the kitchen with our 10 year old daughter, Nettie while Tamsin and Dougal worked on the bowmaking. Nettie and I kept the kettles boiling and cooked cheese toasties over the campfire. We fired up the oven/dryer and enjoyed ourselves baking bread, flapjacks and apple crumble using up the crusts from the toasties along with some damsons to make a bread-and-butter pudding.

Meanwhile in the workshop it became apparent that the lure of the woods was overpowering the kids as they steadily vanished for the rest of the first day. This left the parents to carry out the necessary shaping of the bows with axes and drawknives. Most of us stayed in the woods overnight and started the day with another culinary delicacy of eggs fried in holes cut into sliced of

fried bread, known as 'eggs with hats on'. Back in the workshop the kids joined in with the finishing and tillering of the bows, so that by teatime the bows were completed and they were all ready for some archery. Peter had brought along some bowstrings and arrows and we moved out into the neighbouring field to set up a target on a straw bale. With the exception of one bow (which was later shortened and re-shaped) they all worked superbly. When we switched from shooting at the target to distance shots, everybody was impressed by the distance they could cover, getting on for about a 100 metres.

For the last three years, early autumn has seen an annual 'kindling ceremony' taking place at Brookhouse Wood. During a dry spell in the summer, I fetch a load of softwood offcuts from the local sawmill and cover them up in a corner of the car park. Then one fine Saturday, I chainsaw them into short lengths while half a dozen or so friends use blunt hand axes to split these lengths into little sticks. Within a couple of hours we all have sufficient kindling to get us pretty well through the winter. Meanwhile our kids can get together running riot in the woods and at lunchtime we gather around the campfire to cook the obligatory cheese toasties. In the afternoon parents and kids get together to take down and fold up the huge tarpaulin that has spent the summer sprawling over the workshop roof.

This then neatly wraps up the workshop ready for its winter hibernation until Easter, while I return back to a more domestic routine at home with the family. I liken it to the Alpine existence where the goatherds head off to the hills to spend the summer making the most of the luxuriant summer growth, then return back to the comfort of the village for the winter. In my case I spend the autumn taking a greater role in the housework enabling Tamsin to concentrate on her work producing illustrated stained glass panels ready for the Christmas market. In between housework and childcare I still manage to fit in a number of days offering personal tuition in my workshop at home. When good weather beckons, I get some exercise

OCTOBER

# OCTOBER in Prickly Nut Wood

by sawing and splitting firewood to feed our various woodburners. As the new year commences and the days start to lengthen, the cycle continues and I start thinning the next patch of woodland.

***Below: Kids enjoying toasties and fire.***

With October comes autumn, the final picking of the fruit and in the woodland year a rich tapestry of change, both in the colours and shift of energy, towards winter.

For me it is time to harvest the bulk of my apples. The yield has been good and I have surplus boxes to sell. I sell them to my local greengrocer, Steve Jones, who is always keen to sell local produce. Most commercial orchards have large numbers of trees of only a few varieties, so that they can harvest and sell bulk amounts of apples. In contrast I grow a few trees of many varieties, in some cases just the one tree. What this offers is a flow of apples ripening at different times from late July through to mid November. It offers the greengrocer unusual varieties throughout the growing season. 'Beauty of Bath' rather than 'Discovery'; 'Ribston Pippin' in place of 'Cox's Orange Pippin' (Ribston Pippin is the mother apple of Cox with more vitamin C); 'Annie Elizabeth' as a change from 'Bramleys'; Laxton Superb' – a classic eater, 'Roundway Magnum Bonum' an unusual

***October title page:***
***Prickly Nut Wood oak ablaze in autumnal colours.***

***Above:***
***Spartan growing well on MM106 rootstock at Prickly Nut Wood.***

***Left:***
***Prickly Nut Wood apples for sale at Steve Jones' shop in Fernhurst.***

***Right:***
***Chestnuts roasting in the outdoor kitchen.***

## Cider

I have a small cider press and make a few gallons for home consumption. My press has a wheel turned pulper which mashes the apples prior to them being pressed into juice. A simple press can be constructed with the use of some timber and a car bottle jack to exert the pressure to push out the juice. Apples contain enough sugar to ferment on their own. I wait until the juice has reached blood temperature, add a wine yeast and leave to ferment. Early fermentation is often vigorous, but once calmed it can be left to ferment out in a demijohn with an airlock, as for wine.

lavoured apple for the discerning eater; nd 'Forge' – a classic Sussex cottagers' pple. All of these give the public a wider hoice and hopefully make them aware of our apple eating heritage. A visit to Brogdale in Kent, the national apple collection, will amaze you with the diversity of varieties we have produced. After taking a few boxes to Steve, I have a number ready to store for winter. The rest, and any collected windfalls, mix in with my cider apples to erment over the winter. It should be eady for drinking when coppicing inishes next March.

t is sensible to wear a hat at Prickly Nut Wood at this time of year. Not for the cold, because Octobers are generally mild here, but for protection from falling chestnuts. Contrary to what many people imagine, coppiced chestnut does not produce many nuts. When it does produce, it tends to be on older coppice and in particular along the southern edge of the cant. The trees that produce nuts of a good size are the standards. Branching out high above the coppice, they form plenty of nuts that carpet the woodland floor. Over time, I have noted the most reliable, and the producers of the largest nuts, and have focused my attention on these. Most years provide surplus and some years we are wading in nuts. Low in fat and high in starch, sugar and protein, these nuts are a staple for many countries. With such an abundant food source falling all around me, I am always trying new recipes to enjoy this wild harvest. I clearly remember my first taste of chestnut. I was a young boy taken by the atmosphere and sight of a brazier selling roasted chestnuts on the street. At this time of year, I will often put a few chestnuts to roast over the fire, where they can be enjoyed as a light

## Prickly Nut Wood Soup

This soup has developed over the years and is not easy to give an exact recipe as it is constantly evolving, and is made with regularity each October, but the base of ingredients is fairly constant. The combination of the chestnuts and yeast extract give a meaty flavour that many vegetarians enjoy.

3lb chestnuts
2 onions
1 clove garlic
1 small cooking apple
Few shiitake mushrooms
Seasoning
Olive oil
1 dessert spoon yeast extract
1 teaspoon chopped fresh parsley
Water

Prick and then boil the chestnuts for a few minutes. Cool, then peel and chop. In a deep pan, fry onions and garlic in olive oil until they begin to caramelise. Peel, core and chop apple and add with chestnuts and mushrooms to pan. Once apple has softened, add boiling water to cover and stir frequently. Stir in yeast extract and simmer until chestnuts have softened. Add parsley and serve with crusty bread.

## Training

When I began working in coppice and green wood crafts, it was difficult to gain the experience to learn. There were a few courses on chairmaking and pole lathe construction but little opportunity to work with someone in an 'apprentice' type arrangement. I attended some courses and I am fortunate enough to have the Weald and Downland Open Air Museum near to me as a resource and source of inspiration. I tracked down old coppice workers in the woods, some of whom were helpful while others seemed as if they would rather take their knowledge to the grave than share and pass it on.

Fortunately, this situation has now greatly improved and there are a number of professional woodsman offering types of apprentice-based training. The Bill Hogarth MBE Memorial Apprenticeship Trust (BHMAT) being the most established.

BHMAT was set up, following the death of Bill in 1999, to honour his name and to establish an apprenticeship scheme for coppice workers. Successful applicants for the scheme are placed with a sponsor business for three years and are able to access a wide range of coppice craft courses. They gain the Bill Hogarth Coppice Diploma at the end of their training and receive support to set up their own business. There is now a national scheme which is run from the Green Wood Centre in Shropshire. Between the two organisations a total of 15 apprentices have benefited from this training.

I have been offering places to two or three people each year for the past ten years and now have a diversely structured programme that turns out capable and employable woodsman. I am still in regular contact with most of them and the majority are working and living in the woods. Some are featured in this book.

Choosing applicants is a difficult process. I have requests throughout the year, but I interview in early September and make a decision soon after for them to be ready to start in November, the beginning of my woodland year.

I see this training as a 'lifestyle' training for the next generation. As we move towards a post oil world, our ability to use our hands, to manage the land productively and more in harmony with nature will become increasingly important. If you can turn a tree into a house, turn tree sap to wine, store mushrooms in log piles and have stepped onto nature's time cycle – the woodland year – you will be well prepared for the future. As a woodsman, I see the training of others and the passing on of woodsman's knowledge as our duty as stewards of our woodland heritage.

***Top down:***

***1. Author explaining shingle layout to apprentice roundwood timber framers.***

***2. Learning to use a felling lever.***

***3. Trainees on a roundwood timber framing course.***

snack. Always pierce the skin first or they are liable to explode! Roasted and then dipped in garlic butter is a favourite of mine or dipped in honey if you have a sweet tooth. A favourite recipe I have been refining over a number of years is my Prickly Nut Wood soup.

Autumn is now reaching its crescendo. When you are living in a woodland, the change starts gradually. The subtle deepening of leaf colour day by day can almost go unnoticed until one morning the colour change is distinct and that is a cue for me to take a walk and appreciate the beauty of where I live. I pass some one year old chestnut coppice, now a bronzed fire sweeping across the landscape. It won't be long before winds and frost remove the large leaves and the bare stems that take on an almost purple sheen will stand naked in the landscape. As I descend the hill, I pass the small crimson 'maple leaf' of the wild service tree (*Sorbus torminalis*). The wild service tree is a little known native tree that appears in ancient woodlands, especially on clay soils often in woods of hornbeam, oak or chestnut. At this time of the year, it is covered in small, delicious berries from which it is also given the name 'chequerberry'. These berries, once bletted (softened by frost) or picked and hung up to ripen, have a distinct and unique flavour that I consider to be one of our finest wild fruits. Thirty years ago, you may have found them for sale on a market stall, now your best opportunity of rolling these berries across your taste buds is to harvest from the wild. The seeds within contain very small traces of cyanide, so it is recommended to spit them out. As I spit out a seed, I consider its future and I am reminded of the abundance of tree seed available at this time of year, awaiting collection for propagation. I pick several clusters of berries and put them in my bag. As a timber tree, wild service is rarely available in this country, but in France it fetches a premium as it is sought after by musical instrument makers.

Walking on I am met by the familiar, if rather distasteful smell of the stinkhorn fungus (*Phallus impudicus*). This phallic fungi is sometimes eaten in its jelly like form known as 'witches' eggs' before it emerges, but it has never tempted me. I do not have to walk much further before lunch

***Below: Rich autumn colour of the wild service tree.***

***Below middle: Delicious fruit of the wild service tree.***

***Top left: Shaggy ink cap.***

***Top right: The cardinal beetle* (Pyrochroa coccinea)*, a regular sight at Prickly Nut Wood, adds to the autumn colours.***

***Middle right: Stinkhorn fungus.***

***Below right: A woodland toad.***

appears in the form of the shaggy ink cap (*Coprinus comatus*). This fungi makes an excellent soup and after gathering a dozen or so, I hasten back to the outdoor kitchen. While taking wood from the woodpile, a slight movement reveals the ancient form of the toad (*Bufo bufo*). We look at each other for a while and I feel some guilt at having disturbed its chosen spot for hibernation. The toad eventually retreats back to the woodpile and I continue preparing my fire. Toads will return year after year to their place of birth to breed, sometimes travelling long distances. They are a welcome friend to the gardener, for although they have a taste for the helpful earthworm, they also consume a large amount of slugs.

The fire rises to greet me and I glance across the woodland, glorious in its rich

## Shaggy Ink Cap Soup

½lb shaggy ink caps
1 pint vegetable stock
Seasoning
Butter
¼ pint cream
Parsley

Remove stems and wash and slice ink caps. Fry in butter for five minutes, then add stock and seasoning. Simmer for twenty minutes. Liquidise (not essential) and stir in cream over low heat. Remove from heat into bowls and garnish with parsley.

## Field Maple (*Acer campestre*)

Native broadleaf tree of medium size. Often grown in hedgerows as well as woodlands, striking autumn colour.

*Growing conditions*:
Frequently found in woodlands in association with ash, hazel and oak. Common underwood species throughout England. Prefers heavy (often deep calcerous) soils. Seed often takes two years to germinate in the woodland environment.

*Silvicultural practice*:
Coppices well, usually as part of a mixed broadleaf coppice. Fairly tolerant of shade and occasionally grown as a standard. Reaches maturity in about 50 years.

*Uses*:
Bowls
Carving
Charcoal
Firewood
Furniture
Good host tree for lichens
Musical instruments
Occasional saw log
Pulpwood
Spoons
Turnery
Walking sticks
Wine made from sap (follow birch sap wine instructions – field maple takes longer to collect.)

***Above left: The brightest yellow of our native trees in autumn.***
***Right: Coppiced field maple.***

# OCTOBER in North Wales with Rod Waterfield

autumnal glow and I know winter is not far away. I feel the quickening within me, the need for preparation. I have a young family to keep warm and fed with supplies throughout the winter months, and my instinct is calling me.

I have the great good fortune to own some 50 acres of woodland in North Wales. It is right in the middle of the Clwydian Range Area of Outstanding Natural Beauty and is near to the Offa's Dyke Long Distance Path.

The woodland is a mixture of sites with only about 10 acres having received any management before I bought it. About 20 acres was self-sown on rough grazing which had been abandoned about 50 years ago and about 20 acres was the site of a former sand quarry.

The self-sown area had been colonised first by silver birch, which was reaching the end of its life, and then by sycamore which dominated the wood and needed thinning out to open up the woodland and allow new planting to increase the range of species and widen the age structure. The old sand quarry was full of gorse and rabbits. Some of the gorse was left but most was cut down and mulched and about 7,000 trees were planted in it. Both these areas are being brought into a coppice with standards regime with mainly oak and ash with many stands of hazel. The oak we grow because of its importance as a wildlife habitat; the ash we want, both as standards and coppice, for our craft work; and the hazel we need for coppice work. There is virtually no managed hazel coppice in North Wales and we have had to turn away many requests for hazel hurdles because we cannot get enough good material. Parts of our woodland have stored hazel coppice but it has been left for so long that it does not respond well to coppicing.

In the early days of working in the wood I bought in trees to plant, mainly oak, ash and hazel, from commercial nurseries but now we grow most of what we need from seed collected from local trees.

October is the season when we have to concentrate on collecting seed for our nursery of native hardwood trees. We have developed this over the last fifteen years mostly to provide trees for our own use – some 15,000 on our land and more for planting schemes we have carried out for other people. As we complete the planting on our land, we must develop our sales and this will be a useful part of our business.

There are several reasons why we grow our own trees rather than buy them in. Firstly it saves us money.

***Top:* Rod Waterfield.**

***Left:* Acorns are kept slightly damp through winter and as soon as they start to shoot they are planted into cells.**

Secondly we are growing stock from trees that we know are growing well in our area. Thirdly we are growing trees that have developed as part of an amazingly complex series of interactions between trees and wildlife in this locality. A good example of this is the relationship between the blue tits, the green oak tortrix moth and the oak trees.

Many of our native birds have several broods during the year. Blackbirds for instance have 2-3 broods a year with each brood having 3-5 chicks. This allows the adults to use a variety of food over several months without having too much demand from the chicks at any one time. Blue tits however tend to have just one brood, usually with 10-12 eggs, and the reason for this is that the preferred food for the chicks is young caterpillars, particularly those of the green oak tortrix moth which feed on the buds and young leaves of the oak. The timing of this is very important. The adult moth needs to lay its eggs just as the leaf buds are about to open. The blue tit needs to start laying its clutch so that the eggs hatch just when the caterpillars are reaching their peak. There is some evidence that the blue tit can delay the hatching of the eggs, but only for a few days.

So what has this to do with the trees we plant? One day, after I had been planting young oak trees in the wood, I noticed that the label from the nursery gave the provenance of the seed as Hungary. The trees had been grown within 50 miles of my wood but the seed had been imported from Hungary. I asked the nursery why they were importing acorns and was told that they could not get people in the UK to pick up acorns! I then wondered about the blue tits and the tortrix moths. When my Hungarian oaks grew, would they come into leaf earlier or later than the oaks which were already in the wood? Would the moths be able to adjust to any significant change and, if they could, would the blue tits be able to adjust their breeding pattern as well? I asked everyone I could think of for an answer, from national conservation organisations, to university departments, to local ecologists. Their answer was fairly consistent : We don't know. My response was clear: Collect seed locally and preserve the balance that exists between trees and wildlife.

Collecting seed is fairly straight forward: Collect from more than one tree; choose trees of good form and vigour; avoid trees which are obviously diseased; avoid sites such as parks and gardens where there is a likelihood that trees will have been brought in from outside the area.

There are various strategies for storing seed and treating it before planting but none of it is very complex and you always need to remind yourself that, in the woodland, trees reproduce quite happily without having read any books or gone on any courses.

The problem for us is that large scale nurseries use a huge amount of chemicals to control unwanted plants in the seed beds. For a small scale operation such as ours, we either have to go down the chemical route or carry out a tremendous amount of hand weeding. If you set out fertile, clean seed beds, every weed seed around will say thank you and move in.

We do grow trees in open nursery beds but we also grow trees in cells in a polytunnel. The technique involves waiting till the seed starts to sprout, so that you don't have unviable seed taking up valuable space, and then planting it in its own cell. The cells are in trays of 25 and each cell is open at the bottom. Once the trays have been filled, they are placed on large mesh sheets raised off the ground. When the tap root reaches

***Left: One year old ash grown in a small nursery bed.***

the bottom of the cell it is 'air pruned' and the young tree creates more small fibrous roots. The polytunnel will hold 8,000 cells and has overhead irrigation powered by an electric pump. At the moment we use mains water but we hope to be able to harvest rainwater from the shed roofs and use that. We use peat free compost and make our own by composting the wood residues we have, mainly sawdust and woodchip, with any green material and also the charcoal dust from the kilns. The compost is very low in nutrients, so we use a compound fertiliser in the form of small pellets. These are activated by moisture and warmth and so are only released during the growing season and last for two years, by which time the tree should have been planted out. I am aware that many people would not wish to use any artificial fertilisers but we can see no alternative at the moment.

So what are the benefits of cell grown trees?

- Most trees are ready to plant out after one year rather than about three years with an open bed system
- There is no hand weeding involved which greatly reduces the labour cost
- There is no herbicide use, though fertiliser granules are used
- The cells can be planted out during at least six months of the year as there is no root disturbance and the trees are not stressed by being transplanted.

It is this last benefit that is likely to be the most important. Traditionally trees are lifted at the nursery when they are dormant – some time after they have lost their leaves and before they show signs of new buds. This dormant period used to be from November till February giving four full months for lifting and planting. Recent winters have seen leaves staying on trees till Christmas and new leaves showing in January. If this trend continues, it will be very difficult to lift and replant bare-rooted trees successfully and cell-grown trees may become the norm.

So there is the outline of our small-scale tree nursery using locally collected seed with as little chemical input as possible. We have made one exception to the use of local seed and that is with hazel. The hazel in our wood is of poor quality. It does not respond very well to coppicing or layering, produces few nuts and what it does produce are completely removed by the grey squirrels. After several years of trying to propagate from our own stock, we gave up and bought in seed from the south of England. The results have been spectacular. Excellent quality hazel poles produced in five years from cutting back and so many nuts that the squirrels can't take them all.

Managing your own woodland is very satisfying and particularly so when the trees you see growing are the trees that you have raised from seed. I can cut coppice ash for a course and tell people its whole history.

***Above: One year old rowan grown in cells.***

# Epilogue

I find myself again at that place in time when I am considering which cant of chestnut to cut. I love this land, its heavy soils that cling onto you through the hard toil of winter, and then burst with life in spring from the deep resource of nutrient held within them.

This landscape has been moulded by woodsmen of many generations of which I am lucky to be one. The woodsman is part of this ecosystem, an essential component ensuring habitats continue for the diverse flora and fauna that has evolved over so many years. All this may sound like a romance of the past but the past, present and future are entwined in this cyclical lifestyle. These woods with their sustained yield of timber, are about to come of age once more as we look more locally at our renewable resources.

We should thank the woodsmen of the past whose management shaped these woodlands that I, in the present, keep alive and vibrant, and enjoy the bounty of timber and food that they produce; and you, who are yet to come, who may value them more than I can and learn from them further.

When my apprentices first start I say to them, "see this experience through and you will be initiated into woodland life. You will have changed and there will be no going back to the life you had before."

# About the Author

Ben has always colonised the edge of society. He was educated at six different schools, due to family moves and personal expulsion. He left school at 15 and worked on a smallholding, growing fruit and vegetables and looking after livestock. He spent a year at Sparsholt College where he gained an Advanced National Certificate in Agriculture and then continued working as a shepherd and set up a conservation landscaping business, specialising in ponds and wild flower meadows. Woodlands were a natural progression and after seeking out a few experienced coppice workers, he began work in the woods and in associated coppice crafts.

Ben visited the Amazon in the late 1980s looking for positive solutions to deforestation and on his return set up and directed the charity, The Forest Management Foundation, working primarily with community forestry in Papua New Guinea and was a founding member of the Forest Stewardship Council. The bureaucracy of international forest policy and a realisation that true sustainability begins at home, resulted in his returning to the coppice woods of West Sussex to become a forest dweller. He has lived and worked at Prickly Nut Wood for 16 years, and trains apprentices and runs courses on sustainable woodland management, roundwood timber framing, coppice crafts and permaculture design. Ben helped set up and chaired the Sussex and Surrey Coppice group and also worked for Oxfam as a permaculture consultant in Albania.

He is the author of *The Woodland Way – A Permaculture Approach to Sustainable Woodland Management* and set a precedent in planning law by achieving permission to build his woodland house. The building of the house was filmed for Channel 4's Grand Designs and was voted the winner of the Best Ever Grand Design by public vote and was Grand Designs presenter Kevin McCloud's favourite programme and house build. The story of the construction and build is beautifully choreographed in Ben's second book, *The Woodland House*.

He lives with his wife Bev and has three children and is happiest when he is working on the land.

## Appendix 1

# Appendix 11

# Acknowledgements

For me it has been a personal challenge to balance the writing of this book with the seasonal working of the land and the needs of young children.

Most woodsmen (myself included) are not naturally drawn or inclined towards the technical world of computers and high speed technology, so it has been an extra challenge to work with twelve others, some of whom are 'off-grid' and others fairly nomadic, and co-ordinate their text and photographs. These arrived on a varied range of software programmes and scraps of paper which I then had to try to install onto my ageing and temperamental Apple Mac.

I would like to thank the contributors for their support in this project and for putting time aside in the heart of winter, often after lighting the stove and cooking when most of us are in want of only a chair to collapse into.

I would like to thank all at Permanent Publications for their support; in particular Tim and Maddy Harland, with whom meetings never stay serious for too long, John Adams whose regular repairs of my Mac and web management have ensured I kept going, and Tony Rollinson for organising so much on my behalf.

A special thanks to Dariush, who has shown me such trust and allowed me freedom in the managing of his woodland in conjunction with mine.

As always, a thank you to my family for their support.

A special thanks to my three children Rowan, Zed and Tess, a generation entering a time of change and my wife Bev, who keeps the important flow of family life in order while I am contemplating the behaviour of a shield bug!

# Glossary

**Bender:** Temporary home or shelter made from hazel branches and canvas covering.

**Binders:** Twisted binding between stakes on a layed hedge, usually hazel – also called 'etherings'.

**Bole:** The main stem up to the first side branches.

**Brash:** Small branches from side and top of tree.

**Burr:** Rough growth that develops on the tree, sought after by bowl carvers.

**Cant:** A defined area of coppice, also regionally referred to as a 'panel'.

**Cleave:** To split unsawn timber by forcing the fibres apart along its length.

**Clump:** Small group of trees.

**Coppice:** Broadleaf trees cut during the dormant season, which produce continual multi-stems that are harvested for wood products.

**Coupe:** A felled area of woodland, sometimes coppice

**Crown:** The branches and top of the tree above the bole.

**Fagot:** A tied bundle of small branches traditionally used to fire ovens now used for river bank restoration and coastal defence.

**Glade:** A clearing within the woodland.

**Greenwood:** Freshly cut wood.

**Harr:** Name given to upright part of gate that takes the hinges.

**In-cycle coppice:** Coppice that has been cut at regular intervals and is not overstood.

**Jowl:** The enlarged head of a post (gunstock).

**Layering:** Pegging down a living stem to make it root and create another tree.

**Lop and top:** See brash.

# Appendix III

**Maiden:** Young single stem tree that has not been coppiced.

**Mortise:** A chiselled slot into or through which a tenon is inserted.

**Oigg:** Sussex word for a capping on a gate post.

**Overstood coppice:** Coppice that has not been cut for many years and is out of rotation for usual coppice produce.

**Permaculture:** Ecological design for a sustainable future.

**Pollard:** A tree which has been cut above grazing animal height to allow repeated harvesting of poles from the crown.

**Pleachers:** Partially cut through stems of hedges which are layed at an angle and continue to grow as the sap still flows.

**Ride:** An access route through a woodland often used for timber extraction.

**Rootstock:** The root onto which a scion is grafted.

**Singling:** Converting a coppice stool to a single stemmed tree.

**Slammer:** Name given to upright part of gate that takes the latch.

**Snedding:** Removal of side branches and top of a felled tree.

**Snigging:** Extraction of timber with horses.

**Standard:** A single stemmed tree allowed to grow mature, commonly amongst coppice.

**Stool:** The living stump of a coppiced tree from which new stems grow.

**Stooling:** The earthing up of a stool to ensure regrowing stems produce roots which can be cut and planted as new trees the following winter.

**Suckering:** Regrowth from existing roots of a tree after cutting.

**Tenon:** The projecting end of a timber that is inserted into a mortise.

**Underwood:** Coppice woodland.

**Whip:** A young tree taken from the nursery to be planted out.

**Yurt:** A wooden framed transportable dwelling with canvas covering originating from Asia which is now often used as a dwelling in woodland.

# Contributors

**Ben Law**
Prickly Nut Wood, Lodsworth, West Sussex GU28 9DR
www.ben-law.co.uk

**Alistair Hayhurst**
81 Bournebrook Avenue, Wirksworth, Derbyshire DE4 4BA
01629 824 417
07761 000 590
www.underwoodcrafts.co.uk

**Frankie Woodgate**
Frankie@sylvanenvironmental.com
www.sylvanenvironmental.com

**Peter Broadley**
c/o Old Oxford Cottage, Stoke Bliss, Tenbury Wells, Worcestershire WR15 8QJ
07745 112 426
www.pepperwood.org

**Anthony and Ele Waters**
Pentiddy Wood, Pensilva, Liskeard Cornwall
mail@pentiddy.co.uk

**Mark Howard**
Hannams Farm Cottage, Itchel Lane, Crondall, Hampshire GU10 5PR
07702 152 529
markkit@btinternet.com

**Stewart Whitehead**
Fron Derw, Pontfadog, Llangollen, Wrexham LL20 7AH
Stewart.whitehead@virgin.net

**Geoff Norton and Angela Cole**
Pear Tree Cottage, Whitwell-on-the-Hill, York YO60 7JJ
01653 618 892
Geoff.and.angela@ukonline.co.uk

**Rebecca Oaks**
93 Silverdale Road, Yealand Redmayne, Carnforth LA5 9TD
01524 781 375

**Hugh and Carolyn Ross**
Rawhaw Wood, Pipewell, Nr Kettering, Northamptonshire
www.hazelwoodlandproducts.co.uk

**Paul Morton**
07813 623 985
**Jo Callaghan**
Hill Farm, Stanley Road, Bosbury, Herefordshire HR8 1HE
07969 435 295

**Mike Abbott**
Greenwood Cottage, Bishops Frome, Worcester WR6 5AS
01531 640 005
www.living-wood.co.uk

**Rod Waterfield**
01745 710 626
www.bodfari-charcoal.co.uk
www.woodlandskillscentre.co.uk

# Further Reading

Appendix V

## Books

*Ancient Woodland*; Oliver Rackham; Castlepoint Press, 1980 (new ed. 2003)
The text on ancient woodland. Expensive but essential reading.

*Caring for Small Woods*; Ken Broad; Earthscan, 1998
Practical advice from an experienced forester.

*The Chairmaker's Workshop*; Drew Langster; Lark, 1997
Clear, well photographed, practical guide to Windsor and post and rung chairs.

*The Complete Yurt Handbook*; Paul King; Eco-logic books, 2001
Useful guide to yurt construction.

*Creating New Native Woodlands*; J Rodwell and G Patterson; Forestry Commission Bulletin No: 112, 1994
Useful for species classification.

*EcoForestry*; Alan Drengson and Duncan Taylor; New Society, 1997
Collection of articles, an important read.

*The Encyclopedia of Green Woodworking*; Ray Tabor; Eco-logic Books, 2000
Not an encyclopedia, but a useful green woodworking book with core skills and some patterns included.

*Flora Brittanica*; Richard Mabey; Trafalgar Square, 1996
The evolving culture of our flora.

*Food For Free*; Richard Mabey; Collins, 1989
Fits in your pocket, ideal for a walk in the woods.

*Green Woodwork*; Mike Abbott; Guild of Master Craftsman Publications, 1989
Classic green woodworking text.

*Green Woodworking*; Drew Langster; Lark, 1995
Practical book, good photos and bark peeling section.

*Green Woodworking Pattern Book*; Ray Tabor; Batsford, 2005
Ray's best book, every workshop and green wood worker should have this indispensable guide to patterns on hand.

*Hedging*; Alan Brooks; BTCV, 1998
Useful book on hedge planting and management, good section on regional variations.

*History of the Countryside*; Oliver Rackham; Phoenix Press, 1986
A fascinating description of how the British landscape and human activities have interacted over many centuries to create what we see today.

*Living Wood; Mike Abbott*; Living World Books, 2002
More green woodworking and Mike's journey.

*Make a Chair from a Tree*; John D Alexander Jr; Astragal Press, 1994
Clear and practical chairmaker's guide.

*Making Rustic Furniture*; Daniel Mack; Lark, 1990
Inspirational.

*Practical Forestry for the Agent and Surveyor*; C Hart; Alan Sutton, 1991
Very useful reference book.

*The River Cottage Cookbook*; Hugh Fearnley-Whittingstall; Harper Collins, 2001
Wonderful collection of wild and home produced recipes.

*Silviculture of Broadleaved Woodland*; Julian Evans; Forestry Commission Bulletin No.64, 1984
Highly recommended text.

*The Social Life of Trees*; ed. Laura Rival; Berg, 1998
Anthropological perspective on our relationship with trees.

*This Land Is Our Land*; M Shoard; Gaia Books, 1997
Well researched read on history of land ownership.

*Timber Building in Britain*; R W Brunskill in association with Peter Crawley; Victor Gollancz, 1994
History of timber framing with excellent glossary of terms and techniques.

*Tools and Devices for Coppice Crafts*; F Lambert; Centre for Alternative Technology, 1957
Hard to read but many useful designs.

*Traditional Country Crafts*; J Geraint Jenkins; Routledge and Kegan Paul, 1965
Excellent history of crafts with good photographs, illustrations and a variety of traditional tools.

*Traditional Woodland Crafts*; Raymond Tabor; Batsford, 1994
Well illustrated and practical.

*Trees and Woodlands in the British Landscape*; Oliver Rackham;
Weidenfield and Nicolson, 1995
Excellent historical perspective. Try this first before taking on his Ancient Woodland.

*Understanding the Working Lurcher*; Jackie Drakeford; Crowood Press, 2000
Helpful guide if you are using a working dog in woodland management.

*Wild Flowers of Britain*; Roger Phillips; Macmillan, 1994
Photographically date indicated wild flower identification guide.

*Wild Food*; Roger Phillips; Pan, 1983
Beautifully photographed with good recipes.

*Wood and How to Dry It*; Fine Woodworking Publication; Taunton Press, 1996
Excellent collection of wood drying information and practical designs.

*Woodland Conservation and Management*; G F Peterken; Chapman and Hall, 1981
Nature conservation perspective.

*Woodland Crafts in Britain*; H Edlin; David and Charles, 1973
Classic text, lucky if you find one, needs reprinting!

*The Woodland House*; Ben Law; Permanent Publications, 2004
Journey of building my ecological woodland house.

*Woodlands – A Practical Handbook*; Elizabeth Agate; BTCV, 2002
Useful practical handbook for managing woods.

*The Woodland Way*; Ben Law; Permanent Publications, 2001
Permaculture approach to sustainable woodland management.

## Periodicals

*Crann*
www.crann.ie
Excellent Irish forestry quarterly magazine.

*The Land*
01460 249 204
Chapter7@tlio.org.uk

*Living Woods Magazine*
01285 850 841
info@freshwoodpublishing.com

*Permaculture Magazine*
01730 823 311
www.permaculture.co.uk

*Reforesting Scotland*
0131 554 4321
www.reforestingscotland.org

*Smallwoods*
01952 432 769
www.smallwoods.org.uk

*Woodland Heritage Journal*
01428 652 159
www.woodlandheritage.org.uk

*Wood-lots*
01580 879 552
www.woodnet.org.uk

***Permaculture Magazine and a number of the books listed in this Further Reading appendix – and many others on related subjects – are available from:***

**The Green Shopping Catalogue**
**Permanent Publications**
**The Sustainability Centre**
**East Meon**
**Hampshire**
**GU32 1HR**
**01730 823 311**
**info@permaculture.co.uk**
**www.green-shopping.co.uk**

# Resources

# Appendix VI

## Organisations

**Centre for Alternative Technology**
0845 330 4593
www.cat.org.uk
Resource centre for much of our future needs.

**Chapter 7**
01460 249 204
Chapter7@tlio.org.uk
Help, guidance and campaign for change in the planning system for people genuinely working on the land or needing access to it.

**Permaculture Association (Britain)**
0845 458 1805
www.permaculture.org.uk
Network of people working towards positive change supporting projects, training, networking and research in the field of permaculture.

**Small Woods Association**
01952 432 769
www.smallwoods.org.uk
National charity supporting the management of small woodlands and becoming a national voice and networking centre for small woodland owners and the coppice industry.

**The Association of Pole-lathe Turners (APT)**
01580 240 608
www.bodgers.org.uk
Founded by pole-lathe enthusiasts, now covers many aspects of green woodcrafts. Popular annual gathering and quarterly magazine, The Bodger's Gazette.

**The Forestry Commission**
0845 367 3787
www.forestry.gov.uk
The government agency for forestry offering advice, grants and felling licenses for woodlands.

**The Forestry Contracting Association (FCA)**
0870 042 7999
www.fcauk.com
Trade foundation developing industry standards, insurance, training.

**The Green Wood Centre**
01952 432 769
www.greenwoodcentre.org.uk
Focal point for networking, training, information in greenwood/coppice crafts.

**The Woodland Trust**
01476 581 111
www.woodland-trust.org.uk
Charity conserving and managing woodlands.

**Woodland Heritage**
01428 652 159
www.woodlandheritage.org.uk
Organisation dedicated to improving the quality of trees grown in this country. Hold study days, bursaries for forestry students and publish an excellent quarterly magazine.

## Tools, Equipment and Other Useful Items

**A & F Warehouse**
01428 661 767
www.afwarehouse.co.uk
Mail order supplies of forestry equipment.

**Ann Miller's Speciality Mushrooms**
01467 671 315
www.annforfungi.co.uk
Mushroom spawn supplier.

**Ashem Crafts**
01905 640 070
www.ashemcrafts.com
Producer of rounding and hollow shoulder planes.

**Ashley Iles**
01790 763 372
www.ashleyiles.co.uk
Maker of woodturning tools who take commissions.

**Bill Hogarth MBE Memorial Apprenticeship Trust**
www.coppiceapprentice.org.uk

**British Horse Loggers**
www.britishhorseloggers.org
www.heavyhorses.org

**Chieftan Forge**
01506 652 354
Suppliers of tree planting spades and other forestry tools.

**Green Shopping Catalogue**
01730 823 311
www.green-shopping.co.uk
Useful source of woodland books and tools.

**The Home Brew Shop**
01252 540 386
www.thehomebrewshop.co.uk
Everything you could need for home brewing.

**Ian Swain**
07810 771 122
Reconditioned hand tools.

**Jon Snow – Windy Smithy**
07866 241 783
www.windysmithy.co.uk
Supplier of timber dogs and forged tools.

**Rawnsley Woodland Products**
01208 813 490
www.cornishwoodland.co.uk
Manufactures 'the mule' and many Cornish woodland products for the building industry.

**Ray Iles**
01790 763 406
www.oldtoolstore.com
Son of Ashley, has range of second hand green woodworking tools.

**Steve Darby**
Green Man Ironwork
07771 521 115
Wide range of green wood working tools including stock and hollowing knives, twybils and excellent log dogs.

**Woodland Craft Supplies**
01394 274 419
www.woodlandcraftsupplies.co.uk
Jon Warnes's specialist green wood tools and books supplies.

**The Working Horse Trust**
01892 750 105
www.theworkinghorsetrust.org

# Appendix VII

# Flora & Fauna of Prickly Nut Wood

**Birds recorded by the author at Prickly Nut Wood**

Barn owl
Blackbird
Black cap
Blue tit
Brambling
Bullfinch
Buzzard
Carion crow
Chaffinch
Chiffchaff
Coal tit
Cuckoo
Dunnock
Goldfinch
Greater spotted woodpecker
Great tit
Greenfinch
Green woodpecker
Grey wagtail
Heron
House martin
Jay
Kingfisher
Lesser spotted woodpecker
Long tailed tit
Little owl
Magpie
Mallard
Mistle thrush
Moorhen
Nightjar
Nightingale
Nuthatch
Partridge
Pheasant
Pied wagtail
Redpoll
Redstart
Redwing
Robin
Rook
Song thrush
Sparrow
Sparrowhawk
Starling
Stonechat
Swallow
Tawny owl
Tree creeper
Tree pipit
Willow tit
Woodcock
Wood pigeon
Wood warbler
Wren

**Butterflies recorded by the author at Prickly Nut Wood**

Brimstone
Brown hairstreak
Comma
Common blue
Dingy skipper
Duke of Burgundy
Gatekeeper
Green hairstreak
Green-veined white
Grizzled skipper
Holly blue
Large skipper
Large white
Meadow brown
Painted lady
Peacock
Red admiral
Ringlet
Small tortoiseshell
Small white
Speckled wood
Silver-washed fritillary
White admiral
Wood white

**Plant species recorded at Prickly Nut Wood by Sussex Botanical recording society on a one day visit in July**

| Latin name | Common name |
|---|---|
| *Acer platanoides* | Norway maple |
| *Agrostis canina* | Velvet bent |
| *Agrostis capillaries* agg. | Common bent |
| *Agrostis gigantean* | Black bent |
| *Agrostis stolonifera* | Creeping bent |
| *Ajuga reptans* | Bugle |
| *Alnus glutinosa* | Alder |
| *Anagallis arvensis* | Scarlet pimpernel |
| *Anthoxanthum odoratum* | Sweet vernal grass |
| *Aphanes arvensis* | Parsley-piert |
| *Athyrium filix-femina* | Lady fern |
| *Bellis perennis* | Daisy |
| *Betula pendula* | Silver birch |
| *Betula pubescens* | Downy birch |
| *Blechnum spicant* | Hard fern |
| *Brachypodium sylvaticum* | False brome |
| *Brassica nigra* | Black mustard |
| *Callitriche stagnalis* | Common water starwort |
| *Cardamine flexuosa* | Wavy bittercress |
| *Carex binervis* | Green-ribbed sedge |
| *Carex flacca* | Glaucous sedge |
| *Carex laevigata* | Smooth-stalked sedge |
| *Carex ovalis* | Oval sedge |
| *Carex remota* | Remote sedge |
| *Carex viridula* ssp. *oedocarpa* | Common yellow sedge |
| *Castanea sativa* | Sweet chestnut |
| *Centaurium erythraea* | Common centaury |
| *Cerastium fontanum* | Common mouseear |
| *Circaea lutetiania* | Enchanter's nightshade |
| *Cirsium arvense* | Creeping thistle |
| *Cirsium palustre* | Marsh thistle |
| *Cirsium vulgare* | Spear thistle |
| *Corylus avellana* | Hazel |
| *Crataegus monogyna* | Hawthorn |
| *Crepis capillaries* | Smooth hawk's-beard |
| *Deschampsia flexuosa* | Wavy hair grass |
| *Digitalis purpurea* | Foxglove |
| *Dryopteris affinis* | Scaly male fern |
| *Dryopteris dilatata* | Broad buckler fern |
| *Dryopteris filix-mas* | Male fern |
| *Epilobium ciliatum* | American willowherb |
| *Epilobium obscurum* | Short fruited willowherb |
| *Epilobium parviflorum* | Hoary willowherb |
| *Epilobium tetragonum* | Square-stalked willowherb |
| *Fagus sylvatica* | Beech |
| *Fallopia convolvulus* | Black bindweed |
| *Fragaria vesca* | Wild strawberry |
| *Fraxinus excelsior* | Ash |
| *Galeopsis tetrahit* agg. | Common hempnettle |
| *Gallium aparine* | Cleavers |
| *Gallium palustre* agg. | Marsh bedstraw |
| *Glyceria fluitans* | Floating sweet grass |
| *Gnaphalium uliginosum* | Marsh cudweed |
| *Holcus lanatus* | Yorkshire fog |
| *Holcus mollis* | Creeping soft grass |
| *Hyacinthoides non-scripts* | Bluebell |
| *Hypericum androsaemum* | Tutsan |
| *Hypericum humifusum* | Trailing St John's wort |
| *Hypericum pulchrum* | Slender St John's wort |
| *Hypericum tetrapterum* | Square-stalked St John's wort |
| *Ilex aquifolium* | Holly |
| *Iris pseudacorus* | Yellow Iris |
| *Isolepis setacea* | Bristle Club-rush |
| *Juncus acutiflorus* | Sharp-flowered rush |
| *Juncus articulatus* | Jointed rush |
| *Juncus bufonius* agg. | Toad rush |
| *Juncus bulbosus* agg. | Bulbous rush |
| *Juncus conglomerates* | Compact rush |
| *Juncus effuses* | Soft rush |
| *Juncus tenuis* | Slender rush |
| *Kickxia elatine* | Sharp-leaved fluellen |
| *Larix deciduas* | European Larch |
| *Lonicera periclymenum* | Honeysuckle |
| *Lotus corniculatus* | Common birdsfoot trefoil |
| *Lotus pendunculatus* | Greater birdsfoot trefoil |
| *Luzula multiflora* | Heath woodrush |
| *Luzula pilosa* | Hairy woodrush |
| *Lysimachia nemorum* | Yellow pimpernel |
| *Lythrum portula* | Water purslane |
| *Mentha arvensis* | Corn mint |
| *Moehringia trinervia* | Three-nerved sandwort |
| *Myosotis secunda* | Creeping forget-me-not |
| *Persicaria bistorta* | Common bistort |
| *Persicaria hydropiper* | Water-pepper |
| *Plantago major* | Greater plantain |
| *Poa annua* | Annual meadow grass |
| *Populus tremula* | Aspen |
| *Potentilla erecta* | Tormentil |
| *Potentilla sterillis* | Barren strawberry |
| *Primula vulgaris* | Primrose |
| *Prunella vulgaris* | Selfheal |
| *Pteridium aquiliium* | Bracken |
| *Quercus robur* | Pendunculate oak |
| *Ranunculus repens* | Creeping buttercup |
| *Rhododendron ponticum* | Rhododendron |
| *Rosa* agg. | Wild rose |
| *Rubus fruticosus* agg. | Bramble |
| *Rumex sanguineus* | Wood dock |
| *Sagina procumbens* | Procumbent pearlwort |
| *Salix cinerea* ssp.*oleifolia* | Rusty sallow |
| *Sambucus nigra* | Elder |
| *Scrophularia auriculata* | Water figwort |
| *Scrophularia nodosa* | Common figwort |
| *Scutellaria minor* | Lesser skullcap |
| *Scutellaria x hybrida* | Hybrid skullcap |
| *Senecio jacobaea* | Common ragwort |
| *Senecio sylvaticus* | Heath ragwort |
| *Solanum dulcamara* | Bittersweet |
| *Sloanum nigrum* | Black nightshade |
| *Sonchus oleraceus* | Smooth sow-thistle |
| *Sorbus aucuparia* | Rowan |
| *Stellaria alsine* | Bog stitchwort |
| *Stellaria holostea* | Greater stitchwort |
| *Succisa pratensis* | Devilsbit scabious |
| *Taraxacum* agg. | Dandelion |
| *Taxus baccata* | Yew |
| *Teucrium scorodonia* | Wood sage |
| *Trifolium repens* | White clover |
| *Urtica dioica* | Common nettle |
| *Utricularia vulgaris* agg. | Greater bladderwort |
| *Vaccinium myrtillus* | Bilberry |
| *Veronica arvensis* | Wall speedwell |
| *Veronica beccabunga* | Brooklime |
| *Veronica chamaedrys* | Germander speedwell |
| *Veronica montana* | Wood speedwell |
| *Veronica officinalis* | Heath speedwell |
| *Veronica serpyllifolia* | Thyme-leaved speedwell |
| *Viola riviniana* | Common dog violet |

# Index

## Also by Ben Law

# THE WOODLAND HOUSE

**The building of Ben Law's woodland house was filmed for Channel 4's Grand Designs and was voted the winner of the Best Ever Grand Design of all time by public vote in 2008. It was also Grand Designs presenter Kevin McCloud's favourite programme and house build.**

**The book, *The Woodland House*, is a beautifully illustrated step-by-step guide to how Ben built his handmade home, hewn from his own woodland, placed in a Site of Special Scientific Interest, for under £28,000. It covers all the basics, including why we love to self-build and gives full details of the evolving design process, the identifying of materials, costings, project management and the actual building stages, from foundations and frames, through to interior features. It is the story of how one man turned his dream into a reality through courage, determination, hard work and his innate skill as a designer and craftsman.**

**"Ben Law has proved that it's possible to design and construct an elegant, sophisticated and truly environmentally-friendly home from materials around you, providing you design with diligence and sensitivity. You couldn't find a house that has a more intimate relationship with people and place."**
***From the Foreword by Kevin McCloud, presenter of Channel 4's Grand Designs***

**This is pure permaculture design: a beautiful low impact structure almost entirely resourced from local materials, built by hand by a community of friends and volunteers in total sympathy with the rich ecosystems Ben manages. The house is energy efficient and off-the-grid with no external inputs for heat, light or power and no waste, from the build itself, or today. All greywater and sewage is reused or recycled, rainwater is harvested and reused. The house is surrounded by Ben's companion planted gardens, his chicken runs and further afield, by the chestnut coppice and meadow pasture where his livestock graze.**

**ISBN 1 85623 044 5 250 x 220mm 104pp**
**104 colour photographs, 13 architectural drawings**

**PRICE: £16.95**

**Permanent Publications**
**The Sustainability Centre, East Meon, Hampshire GU32 1HR, UK**
**Tel: 01730 776 582**
**Email: orders@permaculture.co.uk Web: www.permaculture.co.uk**

*"Here is a house so ecologically sound, it breathes in time to the trees around it."*